Basic Mathematics

Quizzes and Tests

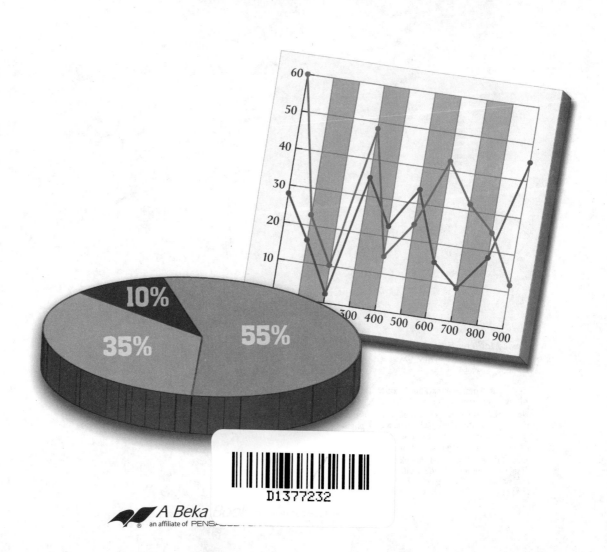

A Beka
an affiliate of PENSACOLA

Teaching Materials

For the Student
Basic Mathematics
Quizzes and Tests

For the Teacher
Basic Mathematics Teacher Key
Curriculum Guide / Solution Key
Teacher Quiz / Test Key

Visual Helps for the Teacher
Concept Cards 5–8
Arithmetic Charts 3–8
Tables and Facts Charts
Rapid Calculation Drills C

***Basic Mathematics* Quizzes/Tests**
For use with fourth edition of text
Editor: C. Sawtelle

To the Teacher

Fifty-four timed speed tests and their cover sheets are in the front section of the Quiz/Test book. An average of two speed tests is given per week. The curriculum directs when the speed tests are given; however, adjustments to fit your schedule can be made since speed tests cover basic skills rather than current concepts.

The 34 quizzes and 12 tests are arranged according to usage. Since quiz gives sections of text that are tested, you can adjust lesson on which you give it as long as all sections have been taught before the quiz. Most of the 12 tests are unit tests. Tests 3, 6, 9, and 12 are cumulative.

The following procedures are suggested for your convenience.

Procedure for Giving Speed Tests

1. Remove Speed Tests 1–15 and corresponding cover sheet from Quiz/Test book and staple together to form a packet. As needed, do the same for Speed Tests 16–27, 28–39, and 40–54.

2. Instruct students to take out sharpened pencil as you distribute speed-test packets. Tell students which speed test they are to complete and time limit. After they write their name/date on speed test, they put pencil down.

3. Instruct class to pick up pencil/begin speed test. Walk around room, making sure students are answering correct speed test.

4. Tell students when to stop. They should stop even if they are not finished. They put pencil in desk and take out a pen.

5. Instruct students to exchange speed tests. Vary method of exchanging (backward, forward, to the right or left).

6. Give correct answers after telling students how many points to deduct for each incorrect answer.

7. Graders should mark incorrect answers with a pen. After all answers are given, they should write score on speed test and on cover sheet. If student is not sure about an answer and what grade to give, he should put a question mark beside score and beside answer he is unsure of. Grader should sign his name at bottom of speed test or beside grade on cover sheet.

8. Grader should then return speed test to owner. If owner thinks grading is not correct, he should put a question mark in pen beside score and beside answer that he wants teacher to check. Packets should be passed to the front.

9. Briefly check speed tests later. Correct any mistakes and write corrected score in red. Circle all correct scores on cover sheet in red. Since all speed tests' scores are recorded on cover sheet, recording them in grade book is not necessary. At end of nine weeks, scores are averaged. **The average is recorded in the grade book as 2 quiz grades.**

Procedure for Giving Quizzes

1. Have quiz ready to distribute to class.

2. Distribute quizzes as you have students take out a pencil and clean cover sheet.

3. Instruct students to show all computation on quiz sheet.

4. After sufficient time, have students put away pencil and take out a pen to grade quiz. (Usually 8 to 10 min. is sufficient time to take / grade quiz.)

5. Give answers to quiz after you tell them how much to deduct for each incorrect answer in each section. Grader should write grade in space marked *Score.*

6. As with speed tests, students should denote questions with a question mark beside questionable answer and score. Students sign their name as grader at bottom of quiz.

7. Students return papers to owners to be checked briefly / passed to front.

8. Later, go through quizzes briefly yourself, checking them, writing grades in red ink, and recording grades.

Procedure for Giving Tests

1. Have students clear desks of everything except 2 clean sheets of paper and 2 sharp pencils with erasers. One sheet of paper is a cover sheet, and the other is a check sheet. Students should write their name on check sheet.

2. Distribute test.

3. Go over directions for each section. Tell students to show their work on test sheet. Check sheet is used to check problems after test is finished.

4. Tell students to write all answers / show all work on test sheet.

5. Collect all tests before end of class. If students finish early, you may want to let them turn in tests / study for another class.

6. Grade tests yourself / record grades. Return graded tests to students as soon as possible. Go over answers / explain any problems that were missed frequently. Answer questions students may have. Collect tests after class has gone over them together.

Averaging Grades

Grades are averaged at end of each nine-week period. In grade book, record grades of tests in red ink and all other grades in blue or black ink. Average a nine-weeks grade in the following way:

1. Average speed test grades. Count speed test average as 2 quiz grades.

2. Average quiz grades including speed test average to get a **daily average,** which counts as one third of nine-weeks grade.

3. Average three-weeks and six-weeks tests to get **test average,** which counts as one third of nine-weeks grade.

4. Nine-weeks test is final one third of nine-weeks grade. Tests 3, 6, 9, and 12 are nine-weeks tests.

5. Semester average is average of two nine weeks in semester.

Name _____

Speed Test	Score
1	_____
2	_____
3	_____
4	_____
5	_____
6	_____
7	_____
8	_____
9	_____
10	_____
11	_____
12	_____
13	_____
14	_____
15	_____

Average [ ]

Speed Test 1 3 min.

Name _____ Date _____ Score _____ 10 each

1.	3,416	2.	1,518	3.	4,000	4.	72,625	5.	8,994
	− 2,305		− 627		− 1,325		− 55,417		− 5,681
	1,111		891		2,675		17,208		3,313

6.	49	7.	44	8.	88	9.	19	10.	235
	+ 28		35		25		18		745
	77		+ 17		+ 45		17		355
			96		158		+ 16		+ 465
							70		1,800

 Speed Test 2 3 min. 30 sec.

Name _____ Date _____ Score _____ 10 each

1.	6,246	2.	87	3.	408	4.	432	5.	35
	× 9		× 26		× 915		763		96
	56,214		2,262		373,320		+ 825		+ 27
							2,020		158

6.	300	7.	1,287	8.	84,972	9.	54	10.	540 ÷ 90
	− 196		− 496		× 5		29) 1,566		6
	104		791		424,860				

 Speed Test 3 2 min. 30 sec.

Name _____ Date _____ Score _____ 2 each

×	9	2	5	11	3	7	4	12	8	6
8	72	16	40	88	24	56	32	96	64	48
6	54	12	30	66	18	42	24	72	48	36
9	81	18	45	99	27	63	36	108	72	54
7	63	14	35	77	21	49	28	84	56	42
12	108	24	60	132	36	84	48	144	96	72

Speed Test 4   3 min.

Name _____   Date _____   Score _____   10 each

1.   9
   7
   3
 + 11
  30

2.   634
 − 287
  347

3. 9,763
×   8
78,104

4.   37
× 26
 962

5.   900
 − 483
  417

6. $9\overline{)29{,}313}$ 3,257

7. $38\overline{)1{,}596}$ 42

8. $430\overline{)3{,}440}$ 8

9. 726 + 394 = __1,120__

10. 417 − 186 = __231__

Speed Test 5   4 min. 30 sec.

Name _____   Date _____   Score _____   10 each

1.   9,327
+ 6,905
16,232

2.   19,016
− 18,473
   543

3.   205
× 53
10,865

4.   7,416
− 1,938
 5,478

5. 97,832
×   9
880,488

6. $44\overline{)1{,}232}$ 28

7.   9,143
 6,809
+ 7,248
23,200

8.   525
× 416
218,400

9. $316\overline{)11{,}692}$ 37

10.   25
× 6
150

Speed Test 6   2 min. 30 sec.

Name _____   Date _____   Score _____   8 each

1. 28 + 56 = __84__

2. 412 − 87 = __325__

3. 600 − 29 = __571__

4. 88 · 10 = __880__

5. 316 ÷ 2 = __158__

6. 146 + 87 = __233__

7. 225 − 163 = __62__

8. 193 · 8 = __1,544__

9. 912 ÷ 3 = __304__

10. 500 ÷ 25 = __20__

11. 716 + 48 = __764__

12. 304 − 12 = __292__

Speed Test 7 4 min.

Name _____ Date _____ Score _____ 10 each

1. $\frac{3}{7}$
         $\frac{1}{7}$
      $+\frac{2}{7}$
      _____
         $\frac{6}{7}$

2. $2\frac{5}{9}$
      $+6\frac{5}{9}$
      _____
         $9\frac{1}{9}$

3. $9\frac{1}{4}$
      $+6\frac{1}{2}$
      _____
        $15\frac{3}{4}$

4. $7\frac{3}{5}$
      $+1\frac{5}{6}$
      _____
        $9\frac{13}{30}$

5. $9\frac{7}{9}$
      $-4\frac{2}{9}$
      _____
         $5\frac{5}{9}$

6. 12
      $-\ \ \frac{1}{2}$
      _____
        $11\frac{1}{2}$

7. $15\frac{3}{4}$
      $-\ 6\frac{1}{3}$
      _____
         $9\frac{5}{12}$

8. $11\frac{5}{8}$
      $-\ 7\frac{3}{4}$
      _____
         $3\frac{7}{8}$

9. 256
      -128
      _____
       128

10. 324
          849
      $+687$
      _____
      $1,860$

 Speed Test 8 2 min. 30 sec.

Name _____ Date _____ Score _____ 10 each

1. $\frac{1}{2} \times \frac{1}{2} = \underline{\frac{1}{4}}$

2. $\frac{3}{8} \times \frac{3}{4} = \underline{\frac{9}{32}}$

3. $\frac{1}{9} \times \frac{1}{5} = \underline{\frac{1}{45}}$

4. $\frac{5}{6} \times \frac{3}{5} = \underline{\frac{1}{2}}$

5. $\frac{2}{9} \times \frac{3}{4} = \underline{\frac{1}{6}}$

6. $1\frac{1}{5} \times \frac{2}{3} = \underline{\frac{4}{5}}$

7. $12 \times \frac{5}{6} = \underline{10}$

8. $\frac{3}{5} \times 10 = \underline{6}$

9. $2\frac{2}{3} \times \frac{1}{4} = \underline{\frac{2}{3}}$

10. $\frac{3}{4} \times \frac{2}{3} = \underline{\frac{1}{2}}$

 Speed Test 9 3 min. 30 sec.

Name _____ Date _____ Score _____ 10 each

1. 5.3
          2.8
      $+7.6$
      _____
       15.7

2. 3.5
      -1.68
      _____
       1.82

3. 2.5
      $\times.69$
      _____
       1.725

4. $.03$
      $\times.02$
      _____
       $.0006$

5. $1.3\overline{)40.3}$ $\ \ \ 31$

6. $\frac{7}{8} \times \frac{2}{3} = \underline{\frac{7}{12}}$

7. $\frac{4}{9} \div \frac{2}{3} = \underline{\frac{2}{3}}$

8. $6 \div \frac{3}{5} = \underline{10}$

9. $5\frac{1}{4}$
      $+9\frac{2}{3}$
      _____
        $14\frac{11}{12}$

10. 1
      $-\ \frac{5}{9}$
      _____
         $\frac{4}{9}$

4

Speed Test 10

2 min.

Name _____ Date _____ Score _____ 10 each

Change to improper fractions.

1. $7\frac{2}{5} = \frac{37}{5}$

2. $12\frac{1}{9} = \frac{109}{9}$

3. $6\frac{3}{8} = \frac{51}{8}$

4. $2\frac{2}{11} = \frac{24}{11}$

5. $10\frac{1}{4} = \frac{41}{4}$

6. $9\frac{5}{7} = \frac{68}{7}$

7. $15\frac{1}{2} = \frac{31}{2}$

8. $11\frac{10}{11} = \frac{131}{11}$

9. $5\frac{7}{8} = \frac{47}{8}$

10. $6\frac{2}{9} = \frac{56}{9}$

Speed Test 11

4 min.

Name _____ Date _____ Score _____ 10 each

1.
```
   975
   629
   713
 + 197
 2,514
```

2.
```
   3,000
 - 1,762
   1,238
```

3.
```
   205
 ×  17
 3,485
```

4. $38\overline{)8,512}$ quotient 224

5.
```
   625
 ×  36
 22,500
```

6.
```
    504
 ×  209
 105,336
```

7.
```
   47,962
 - 29,978
   17,984
```

8. $25\overline{)40,000}$ quotient $1,600$

9.
```
   843
 + 678
 1,521
```

10.
```
   83
 - 16
   67
```

Speed Test 12

2 min. 30 sec.

Name _____ Date _____ Score _____ 2 each

×	9	2	6	8	4	3	12	7	5	11
7	63	14	42	56	28	21	84	49	35	77
5	45	10	30	40	20	15	60	35	25	55
12	108	24	72	96	48	36	144	84	60	132
8	72	16	48	64	32	24	96	56	40	88
9	81	18	54	72	36	27	108	63	45	99

Speed Test 13

3 min. 30 sec.

Name _____ Date _____ Score _____ 12 each

1. 24% of 800
192

2. 75% of 1,000
750

3. 16% of 380
60.8

4. $10\frac{1}{2}$
$+ \ 7\frac{5}{8}$
$18\frac{1}{8}$

5. $10\frac{7}{9}$
$- \ 6\frac{2}{9}$
$4\frac{5}{9}$

6. $3\frac{3}{5}$
$- \ 1\frac{1}{3}$
$2\frac{4}{15}$

7. $2\frac{2}{5} \times \frac{5}{12} = \underline{\ 1\ }$

8. $3\frac{1}{3} \div \frac{5}{6} = \underline{\ 4\ }$

Speed Test 14

3 min. 30 sec.

Name _____ Date _____ Score _____ 7 each

1. 896
432
+ 435
1,763

2. 906
783
+ 842
2,531

3. 5,146
2,907
+ 3,858
11,911

4. 8,719
4,052
+ 1,516
14,287

5. 5,561
7,723
+ 8,406
21,690

6. 83 + 21 = ____104____

7. 172 + 36 = ____208____

8. 526 + 218 = ____744____

9. 103 + 97 = ____200____

10. 66 + 792 = ____858____

11. 799 + 68 = ____867____

12. 894 + 393 = ____1,287____

13. 648 + 75 = ____723____

Speed Test 15

4 min.

Name _____ Date _____ Score _____ 11 each

1. 37.2
15.89
+ 6.79
59.88

2. 11.41
− 6.879
4.531

3. 7.2
× .68
4.896

4. 3.02
× 1.1
3.322

5. $12\frac{1}{2}$
$+ \ 8\frac{2}{3}$
$21\frac{1}{6}$

6. 7
$- \ \frac{3}{4}$
$6\frac{1}{4}$

7. 13
$- \ 8\frac{2}{5}$
$4\frac{3}{5}$

8. $10\frac{1}{2}$
$- \ 3\frac{1}{4}$
$7\frac{1}{4}$

9. $3\frac{2}{9} \times 1\frac{1}{4} = \underline{\ 4\frac{1}{36}\ }$

6

Name _____

Speed Test	Score
16	_____
17	_____
18	_____
19	_____
20	_____
21	_____
22	_____
23	_____
24	_____
25	_____
26	_____
27	_____

Average

Speed Test 16

3 min.

Name _____ Date _____ Score _____ 10 each

1. 5.2 − 3.78 __1.42__	2. 60.9 − 58.723 __2.177__	3. 87.26 − 14.5 __72.76__	4. 99.17 − 42.16 __57.01__	5. 38.4 − 17.836 __20.564__
6. 23 − 19.8 __3.2__	7. 406 − 129.73 __276.27__	8. 25.18 − 17.9 __7.28__	9. 5 − 4.216 __0.784__	10. 839.4 − 8.7 __830.7__

Speed Test 17

2 min.

Name _____ Date _____ Score _____ 2 each

×	5	1	6	3	11	12	10	2	8	9	4	7
12	60	12	72	36	132	144	120	24	96	108	48	84
8	40	8	48	24	88	96	80	16	64	72	32	56
9	45	9	54	27	99	108	90	18	72	81	36	63
11	55	11	66	33	121	132	110	22	88	99	44	77

Speed Test 18

4 min.

Name _____ Date _____ Score _____ 10 each

1. 293 728 642 + 819 __2,482__	2. $42.09 − 37.26 __$4.83__	3. 95 × 8 __760__	4. 392 × 86 __33,712__	5. 8 − 4½ __3½__
6. 375 − 162 __213__	7. 844 + 928 __1,772__	8. 375 × 46 __17,250__	9. $\overset{317}{16\overline{)5,072}}$	10. $\overset{88}{44\overline{)3,872}}$

Speed Test 19   1 min. 30 sec.

Name _____ Date _____ Score _____   5 each

1. 1 qt. = __2__ pt.   2. 1 tbsp. = __3__ tsp.   3. 1 mi. = _5,280_ ft.   4. 1 yd. = __36__ in.

5. 1 m = _100_ cm   6. 1 pk. = __8__ qt.   7. 1 yr. = _365_ da.   8. 1 lb. = __16__ oz.

9. 1 bu. = __4__ pk.   10. 1 hg = _100_ g   11. 1 cm = __10__ mm   12. 1 c. = __8__ fl. oz.

13. 1 decade = __10__ yr.   14. 1 t. = _2,000_ lb.   15. 1 yd. = __3__ ft.   16. 1 mi. = _1,760_ yd.

17. 1 m = _1,000_ mm   18. 1 pt. = __2__ c.   19. 1 km = _1,000_ m   20. 1 wk. = __7__ da.

 Speed Test 20   3 min.

Name _____ Date _____ Score _____   8 each

1. 5 lb. = __80__ oz.   2. 6 c. = __3__ pt.   3. 24 yd. = __72__ ft.   4. 24 ft. = __8__ yd.

5. 102 tsp. = __34__ tbsp. 6. 7 wk. = __49__ da.   7. 7.3 m = _730_ cm   8. .5 km = _500_ m

9. $6\frac{1}{2}$ ft. = __78__ in. 10. 6 qt. = __$\frac{3}{4}$__ pk.   11. 280 cm = _2.8_ m   12. 88 oz. = _$5\frac{1}{2}$_ lb.

 Speed Test 21   4 min.

Name _____ Date _____ Score _____   12 each

1.	2.	3.	4.	5.
45.96	57.3	.972	.913	8.44
72.5	− 19.846	× 6.3	× 7.15	× .958
+ 28.835	37.454	6.1236	6.52795	8.08552
147.295				

6. $\overset{5.6}{.7\overline{)3.92}}$ 7. $\overset{3.6}{52.4\overline{)188.64}}$ 8. $\overset{70}{50\overline{)3,500}}$

Speed Test 22 3 min.

Name _____ Date _____ Score _____ 9 each

1. 19 + 56 = __75__   **2.** 207 + 511 = __718__   **3.** 46 + 38 = __84__

4. 93 + 18 = __111__   **5.** 16 + 35 = __51__   **6.** 94 + 67 = __161__

7.	**8.**	**9.**	**10.**	**11.**
465	1,906	18,375	4,872	925
392	3,782	93,460	9,319	650
+482	+9,654	+87,511	+5,482	+419
1,339	15,342	199,346	19,673	1,994

 Speed Test 23 4 min.

Name _____ Date _____ Score _____ 12 each

1. 12% of 1,250   **2.** 125% of 62   **3.** $8\frac{3}{4}$% of 9,000

150   77.5   787.5

4.	**5.**	**6.**	**7.**	**8.**
.56	843	.043	56.8	97.6
× 2.9	× .19	× .09	× 2.3	× 48.3
1.624	160.17	.00387	130.64	4,714.08

Speed Test 24 4 min. 30 sec.

Name _____ Date _____ Score _____ 10 each

1.	**2.**	**3.**	**4.**	**5.**
.6	5.2	.05	9.17	7.09
× .8	× 17	× 6	× 38.1	× .76
.48	88.4	.3Ø	349.377	5.3884

6. 582)366,078 → 629   **7.** 23)10,189 → 443   **8.** 6.9)34.983 → 5.07   **9.** 246 ÷ 3 = __82__

10. 190 ÷ 10 = __19__

10

Speed Test 25

3 min.

Name _____ Date _____ Score _____ 10 each

| 1. | 57,263
− 18,409
38,854 | 2. | 35,072
− 19,561
15,511 | 3. | 81,097
− 13,896
67,201 | 4. | 10,572
− 9,765
807 | 5. | 15,000
− 9,972
5,028 |

| 6. | 13,573
− 9,584
3,989 | 7. | 56,273
− 19,384
36,889 | 8. | 93,056
− 17,089
75,967 | 9. | 42,625
− 15,416
27,209 | 10. | 60,572
− 18,424
42,148 |

Speed Test 26

4 min.

Name _____ Date _____ Score _____ 10 each

1. $\frac{5}{9} \times \frac{4}{5} = \frac{4}{9}$

2. $1\frac{1}{3} \times \frac{5}{8} = \frac{5}{6}$

3. $\frac{7}{9} \div \frac{3}{8} = 2\frac{2}{27}$

4. $1\frac{1}{2} \div \frac{3}{4} = 2$

5. $15 \times \frac{5}{6} = 12\frac{1}{2}$

| 6. | 973
629
813
+ 782
3,197 | 7. | $9,326.16
− 8,439.38
$886.78 | 8. | 625
× 18
11,250 | 9. | 9.16
× 7.3
66.868 | 10. | $1.2\overline{)2.16}$ 1.8 |

Speed Test 27

3 min.

Name _____ Date _____ Score _____ 2 each

+	25	71	63	19	12	34	58	26	3	42	17	86
32	57	103	95	51	44	66	90	58	35	74	49	118
15	40	86	78	34	27	49	73	41	18	57	32	101
24	49	95	87	43	36	58	82	50	27	66	41	110
9	34	80	72	28	21	43	67	35	12	51	26	95

Speed Test	Score
28	_____
29	_____
30	_____
31	_____
32	_____
33	_____
34	_____
35	_____
36	_____
37	_____
38	_____
39	_____

Average [ ]

Speed Test 28

Name _____ Date _____ Score _____ 10 each

1.
```
       871
312 271,752
```

2.
```
   7,996
   8,495
+  6,293
  22,784
```

3.
```
  12,000
−  6,795
   5,205
```

4.
```
     324
×    682
 220,968
```

5.
```
    .903
×   .004
 .003612
```

6. $\frac{11}{12} \div \frac{4}{5} = \underline{1\frac{7}{48}}$

7. $\frac{2}{7} \times \frac{1}{3} = \underline{\frac{2}{21}}$

8. $3\frac{2}{5} \times 1\frac{1}{2} = \underline{5\frac{1}{10}}$

9. $1\frac{3}{4} \div 1\frac{3}{4} = \underline{1}$

10. $12 \times \frac{1}{2} = \underline{6}$

Speed Test 29

Name _____ Date _____ Score _____ 10 each

1.
```
   73,206
−  16,819
   56,387
```

2.
```
     725
×    416
 301,600
```

3.
```
   7.12
−  6.093
   1.027
```

4.
```
    8.05
×   .019
 .15295
```

5.
```
   8,432
   6,758
+  1,033
  16,223
```

6.
```
  $25.18
−  16.55
   $8.63
```

7.
```
     518
×     24
  12,432
```

8.
```
   1 3/8
+  1 1/4
   2 5/8
```

9.
```
   16 1/2
−   7 3/4
    8 3/4
```

10.
```
    1.3
−  0.975
   0.325
```

Speed Test 30

Name _____ Date _____ Score _____ 10 each

1. $68 \cdot 3 = \underline{204}$

2. $9 \cdot 42 = \underline{378}$

3. $18 \cdot 20 = \underline{360}$

4. $12 \cdot 11 = \underline{132}$

5. $400 \cdot 51 = \underline{20,400}$

6.
```
   5,432
   7,905
   3,842
+  8,409
  25,588
```

7.
```
   19,000
   47,062
   38,329
+  44,786
  149,177
```

8.
```
   8,416
   7,923
   5,416
+  6,382
  28,137
```

9.
```
    416
    384
    625
    827
+   593
  2,845
```

10.
```
    93
    79
    83
    14
+   89
   358
```

Speed Test 31

1 min. 45 sec.

Name _____ Date _____ Score _____ 2 each

×	4	10	7	6	12	9	2	5	11	8	3	1
9	36	90	63	54	108	81	18	45	99	72	27	9
11	44	110	77	66	132	99	22	55	121	88	33	11
7	28	70	49	42	84	63	14	35	77	56	21	7
12	48	120	84	72	144	108	24	60	132	96	36	12

Speed Test 32

4 min.

Name _____ Date _____ Score _____ 10 each

1.
$$
\begin{array}{r}
8,376 \\
5,924 \\
+\ 9,783 \\
\hline
24,083
\end{array}
$$

2.
$$
\begin{array}{r}
60,572 \\
-\ 19,824 \\
\hline
40,748
\end{array}
$$

3.
$$
\begin{array}{r}
618 \\
\times\ 412 \\
\hline
254,616
\end{array}
$$

4.
$$
\begin{array}{r}
\frac{2}{9} \\
\frac{1}{3} \\
+\ \frac{1}{2} \\
\hline
1\frac{1}{18}
\end{array}
$$

5.
$$
\begin{array}{r}
6\frac{1}{2} \\
-\ \frac{3}{4} \\
\hline
5\frac{3}{4}
\end{array}
$$

6. $\frac{9}{10} \times \frac{5}{6} = \underline{\ \frac{3}{4}\ }$

7. $1\frac{1}{2} \div \frac{3}{4} = \underline{\ 2\ }$

8.
$$
\begin{array}{r}
9.37 \\
-\ 6.803 \\
\hline
2.567
\end{array}
$$

9.
$$
\begin{array}{r}
.006 \\
\times\ .7 \\
\hline
.0042
\end{array}
$$

10. $8\overline{)1.6}$ = .2

Speed Test 33

2 min.

Name _____ Date _____ Score _____ 10 each

1. $\frac{3}{8} = \frac{9}{24}$

2. $\frac{4}{5} = \frac{20}{25}$

3. $\frac{9}{11} = \frac{72}{88}$

4. $\frac{32}{36} = \frac{8}{9}$

5. $\frac{7}{10} = \frac{49}{70}$

6. $9\frac{7}{8} \div 9\frac{7}{8} = \underline{\ 1\ }$

7. $2\frac{9}{10} \times 1 = \underline{\ 2\frac{9}{10}\ }$

8. $\frac{\frac{13}{20}}{\frac{13}{20}} = \underline{\ 1\ }$

9. $\frac{1}{4}$ in. = 50 mi.

$\underline{\ 2\frac{1}{2}\ }$ in. = 500 mi.

10. 1 mm = 10 km

59 mm = __590__ km

Copyright © mmi Pensacola Christian College • Not to be reproduced.

15

Speed Test 34

3 min.

Name _____ Date _____ Score _____ 10 each

1. 38
    49
    76
    + 63
    ‾‾‾‾‾
    226

2. .073
    9.16
    .392
    + 8.146
    ‾‾‾‾‾‾
    17.771

3. 32,057
    85,625
    + 11,462
    ‾‾‾‾‾‾‾
    129,144

4. $29.35
    62.87
    + 25.42
    ‾‾‾‾‾‾
    $117.64

5. 310
    496
    + 725
    ‾‾‾‾‾
    1,531

6. 12
    − 4.682
    ‾‾‾‾‾‾
    7.318

7. 9.7
    − 6.324
    ‾‾‾‾‾
    3.376

8. 83.629
    − 14.8
    ‾‾‾‾‾
    68.829

9. 137,216
    − 43,829
    ‾‾‾‾‾‾
    93,387

10. 72,146
    − 16,948
    ‾‾‾‾‾‾
    55,198

Speed Test 35

3 min. 30 sec.

Name _____ Date _____ Score _____ 10 each

1. 385
    296
    432
    + 354
    ‾‾‾‾‾
    1,467

2. 135
    × 24
    ‾‾‾‾‾
    3,240

3. 5,000
    × 20
    ‾‾‾‾‾
    100,000

4. .007
    × .006
    ‾‾‾‾‾
    .000042

5. $\frac{729}{9}$ = _81_

6. 29.4
    × .195
    ‾‾‾‾‾
    5.733

7. 7.1
    − 6.284
    ‾‾‾‾‾
    0.816

8. $\frac{256}{4}$ = _64_

9. $2.1\overline{)8.4}$ → 4

10. $.46\overline{)15.134}$ → 32.9

Speed Test 36

3 min. 30 sec.

Name _____ Date _____ Score _____ 10 each

1. 52.6
    7.89
    + 37.95
    ‾‾‾‾‾
    98.44

2. 20.4
    − 7.956
    ‾‾‾‾‾
    12.444

3. $\frac{3}{8}$
    $\frac{5}{6}$
    + $\frac{1}{2}$
    ‾‾‾‾‾
    $1\frac{17}{24}$

4. $11\frac{3}{4}$
    − $7\frac{5}{6}$
    ‾‾‾‾‾
    $3\frac{11}{12}$

5. $3\frac{1}{2} \div \frac{7}{8}$ = _4_

6. $1\frac{1}{2} \times \frac{3}{5}$ = _$\frac{9}{10}$_

7. $37.86
    29.45
    + 96.32
    ‾‾‾‾‾
    $163.63

8. $\frac{328}{8}$ = _41_

9. $\frac{6}{7} \times \frac{7}{6}$ = _1_

10. −8 + (−8) = _−16_

16

Name _____ Date _____ Score _____   8 each

1. 5^2	2. 12^2	3. 7^2	4. 6^2	5. 1^2	6. 8^2	7. 10^2
25	144	49	36	1	64	100

8. $\begin{array}{r} 327 \\ -\ 263 \\ \hline 64 \end{array}$ 9. $\begin{array}{r} 508 \\ -\ 429 \\ \hline 79 \end{array}$ 10. $\begin{array}{r} 1{,}736 \\ -\ 839 \\ \hline 897 \end{array}$ 11. $\begin{array}{r} 23{,}014 \\ -\ 16{,}082 \\ \hline 6{,}932 \end{array}$ 12. $\begin{array}{r} \$162.15 \\ -\ 97.89 \\ \hline \$64.26 \end{array}$

Name _____ Date _____ Score _____   2 each

×	9	7	5	3	4	11	2	6	12	8
8	72	56	40	24	32	88	16	48	96	64
7	63	49	35	21	28	77	14	42	84	56
12	108	84	60	36	48	132	24	72	144	96
6	54	42	30	18	24	66	12	36	72	48
9	81	63	45	27	36	99	18	54	108	72

Name _____ Date _____ Score _____   8 each

1. $\sqrt{25}$	2. $\sqrt{64}$	3. $\sqrt{144}$	4. 8^2	5. 15^2	6. 2^3
5	8	12	64	225	8

7. $-4 + (-2) = \underline{\ -6\ }$ 8. $15 + (-10) = \underline{\ 5\ }$ 9. $-8 + 6 = \underline{\ -2\ }$

10. $-3 - (-3) = \underline{\ 0\ }$ 11. $5(-4) = \underline{\ -20\ }$ 12. $\dfrac{-20}{-5} = \underline{\ 4\ }$

Name _____

Speed Test	Score
40	_____
41	_____
42	_____
43	_____
44	_____
45	_____
46	_____
47	_____
48	_____
49	_____
50	_____
51	_____
52	_____
53	_____
54	_____

Average

Speed Test 40

2 min. 30 sec.

Name _____ Date _____ Score _____ 9 each

1. 1 gal. = __4__ qt. **2.** 1 da. = __24__ hr. **3.** 1 L = __.1__ daL **4.** 1 century = __100__ yr.

5. 1 bu. = __4__ pk. **6.** 1 cg = __10__ mg **7.** 1 tbsp. = __3__ tsp. **8.** 1 mi. = _1,760_ yd.

9. $3\frac{1}{2}$ lb. = __56__ oz. **10.** 325 yr. = _32.5_ decades **11.** 23.5 hg = _2.35_ kg

Speed Test 41

2 min. 30 sec.

Name _____ Date _____ Score _____ 6 each

1. $-5 - (-6) =$ __1__ **2.** $14 + (-8) =$ __6__ **3.** $-7 + (-5) =$ _−12_

4. $-12 + 9 =$ _−3_ **5.** $7 - 8 =$ _−1_ **6.** $13 + (-2) =$ __11__

7. $5(-6) =$ _−30_ **8.** $-8(-4) =$ __32__ **9.** $-12(5) =$ _−60_

10. $\frac{-36}{-9} =$ __4__ **11.** $\frac{18}{-2} =$ _−9_ **12.** $\frac{-32}{8} =$ _−4_

13. $\sqrt{100} =$ __10__ **14.** $5^2 =$ __25__ **15.** $2^5 =$ __32__

Speed Test 42

3 min.

Name _____ Date _____ Score _____ 10 each

1.
$$\begin{array}{r} 9,764 \\ 8,209 \\ + 5,619 \\ \hline 23,592 \end{array}$$

2.
$$\begin{array}{r} 11,304 \\ - 9,782 \\ \hline 1,522 \end{array}$$

3.
$$\begin{array}{r} 946 \\ \times 872 \\ \hline 824,912 \end{array}$$

4. $572\overline{)60,060}$ = 105

5. $\frac{1}{2} \times \frac{1}{2} = \frac{1}{4}$

6.
$$\begin{array}{r} .916 \\ \times .007 \\ \hline .006412 \end{array}$$

7. $1.8\overline{)57.6}$ = 32

8.
$$\begin{array}{r} 5.2 \\ - 3.87 \\ \hline 1.33 \end{array}$$

9.
$$\begin{array}{r} 629 \\ + 486 \\ \hline 1,115 \end{array}$$

10.
$$\begin{array}{r} 5,932 \\ + 6,809 \\ \hline 12,741 \end{array}$$

Speed Test 43   2 min. 30 sec.

Name _____ Date _____ Score _____   10 each

Write the area formulas.

1. rectangle   **2.** square   **3.** triangle   **4.** trapezoid

$A = $ ___ *lw* ___ $A = $ ___ s^2 ___ $A = $ ___ $\frac{1}{2}bh$ ___ $A = $ ___ $\frac{h(b_1 + b_2)}{2}$ ___

Square.

5. 11	**6.** 34	**7.** 2.3	**8.** $\frac{3}{4}$	**9.** 1.06	**10.** 250
121	1,156	5.29	$\frac{9}{16}$	1.1236	62,500

 Speed Test 44   4 min.

Name _____ Date _____ Score _____   10 each

1.   9,736
  2,509
  5,843
+ 7,824
———
25,912

2.   957
× 56
———
53,592

3.   40,635
− 19,782
———
20,853

4. −12 − (−6)
−6

5.   32,756
− 19,785
———
12,971

6.   .54
× 9.6
———
5.184

7.   3.2
− 2.9763
———
0.2237

8.   19,762
  48,795
+ 83,987
———
152,544

9.   586
× 295
———
172,870

10. 318⟌506 $\overset{1.6}{}$ (nearest tenth)

Speed Test 45   3 min. 30 sec.

Name _____ Date _____ Score _____   10 each

1.   372
  635
  849
+ 276
———
2,132

2. 4^3
64

3.   842
× 75
———
63,150

4. $\frac{-50}{-10}$
5

5.   83,241
− 16,876
———
66,365

6. 4.3⟌13.76 $\overset{3.2}{}$

7.   593
× 782
———
463,726

8.   4,973
  8,706
+ 6,592
———
20,271

9.   50,000
− 17,640
———
32,360

10. $\sqrt{121}$
11

Speed Test 46

2 min.

Name _____ Date _____ Score _____ 10 each

1. $\frac{-18}{6}$

-3

2. -3(4)

-12

3. -11
    - (+3)
    ―――
    -14

4. 13
    + (-6)
    ―――
    7

5. 5(-8)

-40

6. -9(-3)

27

7. $\frac{-25}{5}$

-5

8. 24
    - (-8)
    ―――
    32

9. -15
    - (-6)
    ―――
    -9

10. $\frac{16}{-4}$

-4

Speed Test 47

3 min.

Name _____ Date _____ Score _____ 10 each

1. $6^2 =$ ___36___

2. $5^2 =$ ___25___

3. $11^2 =$ ___121___

4. $3^3 =$ ___27___

5. $7^4 =$ ___2,401___

6. $19^2 =$ ___361___

7. $8^5 =$ ___32,768___

8. $4^3 =$ ___64___

9. $13^2 =$ ___169___

10. $25^3 =$ ___15,625___

Speed Test 48

1 min. 45 sec.

Name _____ Date _____ Score _____ 2 each

×	10	6	12	2	3	8	11	5	9	4
11	110	66	132	22	33	88	121	55	99	44
9	90	54	108	18	27	72	99	45	81	36
12	120	72	144	24	36	96	132	60	108	48
6	60	36	72	12	18	48	66	30	54	24
8	80	48	96	16	24	64	88	40	72	32

Speed Test 49

3 min. 30 sec.

Name _____ Date _____ Score _____ 10 each

| 1. | 8,432
6,759
7,846
+ 3,804
26,841 | 2. | 18,506
38,419
+ 57,895
114,820 | 3. | 765,342
849,715
+ 811,995
2,427,052 | 4. | 28,496
3,805
76,624
+ 89,317
198,242 | 5. | 95,726
+ 82,484
178,210 |

| 6. | 18,216
− 7,935
10,281 | 7. | 84,703
− 69,729
14,974 | 8. | 60,000
− 19,789
40,211 | 9. | 4,816
− 1,705
3,111 | 10. | 234,783
− 194,891
39,892 |

Speed Test 50

1 min. 30 sec.

Name _____ Date _____ Score _____ 10 each

1. $5(-3)$

-15

2. $-17 - (-3)$

-14

3. $-6 + (-8)$

-14

4. $12(3)$

36

5. $-6(-5)$

30

6. $\dfrac{-121}{11}$

-11

7. $\dfrac{-18}{-6}$

3

8. $8 - (-5)$

13

9. $9 + (-3)$

6

10. $-5(4)$

-20

Speed Test 51

2 min. 30 sec.

Name _____ Date _____ Score _____ 11 each

Circle	Radius	Diameter	Circumference	Area
1	1 in.	2 in.	6.28 in.	3.14 sq. in.
2	2 cm	4 cm	12.56 cm	12.56 cm^2
3	10 in.	20 in.	62.8 in.	314 sq. in.

Name _____ Date _____ Score _____ 2 each

×	7	2	11	8	12	5	9	6	10	4
9	63	18	99	72	108	45	81	54	90	36
11	77	22	121	88	132	55	99	66	110	44
8	56	16	88	64	96	40	72	48	80	32
12	84	24	132	96	144	60	108	72	120	48
6	42	12	66	48	72	30	54	36	60	24

Name _____ Date _____ Score _____ 10 each

1. $\begin{array}{r} 832 \\ 629 \\ 548 \\ +706 \\ \hline 2,715 \end{array}$

2. $\sqrt{625}$
   25

3. 3^3
   27

4. $\begin{array}{r} -26 \\ -13 \\ \hline 2 \end{array}$

5. $\begin{array}{r} 5.06 \\ \times\,.78 \\ \hline 3.9468 \end{array}$

6. $\begin{array}{r} 2,307 \\ -1,563 \\ \hline 744 \end{array}$

7. $-8(4)$
   -32

8. $\begin{array}{r} 34,163 \\ -19,485 \\ \hline 14,678 \end{array}$

9. $14\overline{\smash)8{,}890}$ = 635

10. $\dfrac{-81}{9}$
    -9

Name _____ Date _____ Score _____ 10 each

1. $\begin{array}{r} \frac{5}{8} \\ \frac{1}{8} \\ +\frac{3}{8} \\ \hline 1\frac{1}{8} \end{array}$

2. $\begin{array}{r} 5\frac{3}{5} \\ 6\frac{1}{3} \\ +7\frac{1}{2} \\ \hline 19\frac{13}{30} \end{array}$

3. $\begin{array}{r} 11\frac{5}{9} \\ 18\frac{2}{3} \\ +7\frac{1}{3} \\ \hline 37\frac{5}{9} \end{array}$

4. $\begin{array}{r} 11 \\ -3\frac{2}{5} \\ \hline 7\frac{3}{5} \end{array}$

5. $\begin{array}{r} 16\frac{1}{2} \\ -7\frac{5}{8} \\ \hline 8\frac{7}{8} \end{array}$

6. $\frac{3}{8} \times \frac{4}{15} = \underline{\frac{1}{10}}$

7. $12 \times \frac{7}{8} = \underline{10\frac{1}{2}}$

8. $1\frac{1}{2} \times 1\frac{1}{3} = \underline{2}$

9. $15 \div \frac{3}{5} = \underline{25}$

10. $\frac{5}{9} \div \frac{10}{11} = \underline{\frac{11}{18}}$

Name _____ Date _____ Score _____

QUIZ 1

Basic Mathematics

Unit 1 (1.1–1.5)

Write *true* or *false* in each blank. *5 each*

1. _____true_____ The value of 7 in 57,418 is 7,000.

2. _____false_____ The answer in a subtraction problem is called the remainder.

3. _____false_____ Any number multiplied by zero is that number.

4. _____false_____ In the number 444, all the digits have the same value.

5. _____true_____ The order of the addends may be switched without changing the sum.

6. _____false_____ A plus sign (+) or a raised dot (·) may be used to indicate addition.

7. _____false_____ The order of the minuend and the subtrahend in a subtraction problem may be switched without changing the difference.

8. _____true_____ Estimation is the first step in division whenever the divisor has more than one digit.

9. _____false_____ The value of 6 in 7,685 is greater than the value of 6 in 6,785.

10. _____true_____ The product of 8 × 4 × 6 × 0 × 3 × 9 is 0.

Find the answers. *10 each*

11.
```
  9,738
  6,209
 +5,896
 ------
 21,843
```

12.
```
  29,736
 -18,938
 -------
  10,798
```

13.
```
    438
  ×  73
 ------
 31,974
```

14.
```
   236
 × 405
 ------
 95,580
```

15.
```
     418
 56)23,408
```

Name _____ Date _____ Score _____

Unit 1 (1.6–1.14)

Write *true* or *false* in each blank. *5 each*

1. _____false_____ A whole number with 6 digits contains millions.

2. _____false_____ The Roman numeral for zero is Z.

3. _____true_____ For a number to be divisible by 6, the number must be even and divisible by 3.

4. _____false_____ For a number to be divisible by 9, the number must be odd and the sum of the digits must be divisible by 9.

5. _____true_____ The number 1 is neither prime nor composite.

Follow the directions. *7 each*

6. _____7,386,210_____ Round off 7,386,209 to the nearest ten.

7. _____3,000,000_____ Round off 2,992,576 to the nearest hundred thousand.

8. _____761,000,000_____ Round off 761,489,999 to the nearest one million.

9. _____2,464_____ Write MMCDLXIV using Arabic numerals.

10. _____$1,500_____ Find the cost of four collie puppies if each puppy costs $375.

11. _____$6.21_____ Find the change from a one-hundred dollar bill if the items cost $35.89, $18.91, and $38.99.

12. _____$27_____ Find the cost of one book if eight identical books cost $216.

13. _____50_____ Divide 45,000 by 900.

14. _____9,000,023,000_____ Use digits to write nine billion, twenty-three thousand.

15. _____146,124_____ Multiply 451 times 324 and check by casting out 9s.

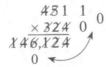

Name _____ Date _____ Score _____

QUIZ 3   *Basic Mathematics*

Unit 1 (1.1–1.17)

Follow the directions.   *5 each*

1. _____$18 = 2 \times 3 \times 3$_____ Write the prime factors of 18.

2. _____4_____ Find the greatest common factor of 8 and 12.

3. _____1_____ Write the counting number that is neither prime nor composite.

4. _____1,549_____ Write the Arabic value of MDXLIX.

5. _____15,007,000,016_____ Use digits to write fifteen billion, seven million, sixteen.

6. _____1,324_____ Choose the number that is divisible by 4: 1,342 or 1,324.

7. _____23,895,800_____ Round off 23,895,796 to the nearest ten.

8. _____85_____ Find the average of 84, 93, 77, and 86.

Find the answers. Check problem 9 by casting out 9s.   *10 each*

9.

```
  5,634  0
  2,573  8       7
  9,621  0      ↗
+ 8,792  8
 26,620
     7 ←
```

10.
```
   21,386
 −  7,389
   13,997
```

11.
```
   15,000
 − 13,296
    1,704
```

12.
```
    375
 ×   58
 21,750
```

13. 630)‾2‾5‾,‾2‾0‾0‾   quotient 40

14. 19)‾1‾,‾6‾5‾3‾   quotient 87

TEST 1   *Basic Mathematics*

Unit 1

Find the answers. Check problem 10 by casting out 9s. Show all of your work.

3 each (30)

1. ___2,032___

$$
\begin{array}{r}
1.\quad 427 \\
855 \\
524 \\
46 \\
+\,180 \\
\end{array}
\qquad
\begin{array}{r}
2.\quad 2,649 \\
3,558 \\
4,164 \\
+\ 307 \\
\end{array}
\qquad
\begin{array}{r}
3.\quad 9,452 \\
-\,4,959 \\
\end{array}
\qquad
\begin{array}{r}
4.\quad 16,000 \\
-\ 7,281 \\
\end{array}
$$

2. ___10,678___

3. ___4,493___

4. ___8,719___

$$
\begin{array}{r}
5.\quad 79 \\
\times\,28 \\
\end{array}
\qquad
\begin{array}{r}
6.\quad 7,034 \\
\times\ 951 \\
\end{array}
\qquad
\begin{array}{r}
7.\quad 384 \\
\times\,906 \\
\end{array}
\qquad
8.\ 90\overline{)3,600}
$$

5. ___2,212___

6. ___6,689,334___

7. ___347,904___

8. ___40___

9. $66\overline{)117,216}$

10. $315\overline{)164,115}$

$$
\begin{array}{r}
8 \\
0\quad\ 521 \\
\end{array}
$$

$0 \times 8 = 0$

9. ___1,776___

10. ___521___

Round off 4,638,482,196 as directed in problems 11 to 15. *2 each (10)*

11. ___5,000,000,000___   nearest one billion

12. ___4,638,482,200___   nearest ten

13. ___4,638,482,000___   nearest one thousand

14. ___4,640,000,000___   nearest ten million

15. ___4,600,000,000___   nearest hundred million

Follow the directions. Show all of your work. *2 each (24)*

16. _____300_____ Find the product of 25 · 12.

17. _____310_____ Average 273, 358, 294, 306, 288, and 341.

18. ___403,000,065,011___ Use digits to write four hundred three billion, sixty-five thou-
                           sand, eleven.

19. _____2,642_____ Write the Arabic value of MMDCXLII.

20. _____783_____ Choose the number that is divisible by 9: 574 or 783.

21. _24 = 2 × 2 × 2 × 3_ Write the prime factors of 24.

22. _16 = 2 × 2 × 2 × 2_ Write the prime factors of 16.

23. __42 = 2 × 3 × 7__ Write the prime factors of 42.

24. _____6_____ Find the greatest common factor for 12 and 18.

25. _____30_____ Find the least common multiple of 5 and 6.

26. _____12_____ Write the least common multiple of 4 and 6.

27. _____2_____ Write the greatest common factor of 4 and 6.

28. Mark under the three numbers that are divisible by 4. *1 each (3)*

300	128	442	1,566	2,024	182
●	●	○	○	●	○

29. Mark under the three numbers that are divisible by 6. *1 each (3)*

672	411	3,022	1,584	657	906
●	○	○	●	○	●

Write *true* or *false* in each blank.   *2 each (14)*

30. ____false____   The number 1 is a prime number.

31. ____false____   The number 2 is a composite number.

32. ____true____   The order of the factors can be switched without changing the product.

33. ____false____   The sum of any number and 1 is that number.

34. ____true____   The greatest common factor for 6 and 9 is 3.

35. ____false____   The least common multiple for 3, 4, and 5 is 20.

36. ____false____   MCCCXXXVI = 3,326

Solve the word problems. Show all of your work.   *4 each (12)*

37. ___156 dogs and cats___   The Ellis Animal Shelter had 52 dogs on Saturday. The shelter had twice as many cats as dogs. How many dogs and cats did the shelter have on Saturday altogether?

38. _____480,000_____   The population of Reidville is 478,967. Round off the population to the nearest ten thousand.

39. _____$454_____   Colin's grandparents sent him a check for one thousand dollars. Colin gave $150 to his church, and he spent $396 on school clothes, books, and supplies. How much of the money does he have left?

Name _____ Date _____ Score _____

Unit 2 (2.1–2.6)

Write *true* or *false* in each blank.   *6 each*

1. _____true_____ The denominator is the bottom number in a fraction, and it indicates how many parts the whole is divided into.

2. _____false_____ To reduce a fraction to lowest terms, divide both terms by the least common multiple.

3. _____false_____ Because $\frac{1}{2}$ is the reduced form of $\frac{2}{4}$, $\frac{1}{2}$ of a pizza is less than $\frac{2}{4}$ of the same pizza.

4. _____true_____ $3\frac{7}{8}$ is an example of a mixed number.

5. _____false_____ Fractions must have a common numerator before they can be added.

Follow the directions.   *6 each*

6. _____$\frac{5}{6}$_____ Reduce $\frac{10}{12}$ to lowest terms.

7. _____$\frac{8}{3}$_____ Change $2\frac{2}{3}$ to an improper fraction.

8. _____$4\frac{1}{4}$_____ Change $\frac{17}{4}$ to a mixed number.

9. _____4_____ Change $\frac{36}{9}$ to a whole number.

10. _____$7\frac{10}{11}$_____ Add $2\frac{3}{11}$, $5\frac{4}{11}$, and $\frac{3}{11}$.

Find the answers.   *10 each*

11. $\quad 8\frac{4}{9}$
$\quad\quad 7\frac{2}{3}$
$\quad + 2\frac{1}{6}$
$\quad\quad\overline{18\frac{5}{18}}$

12. $\quad 13$
$\quad - 6\frac{3}{4}$
$\quad\quad\overline{6\frac{1}{4}}$

13. $\quad 10\frac{2}{5}$
$\quad - 4\frac{1}{3}$
$\quad\quad\overline{6\frac{1}{15}}$

14. $\frac{5}{8} \times \frac{3}{4} = \underline{\frac{15}{32}}$

QUIZ 5   *Basic Mathematics*

Units 2–3 (2.7–3.6)

Follow the directions. *6 each*

1. _____.09_____ Write $\frac{9}{100}$ as a decimal.

2. ____$\frac{3}{1,000}$____ Write .003 as a fraction.

3. _____.1_____ Choose the greater: .007 or .1.

4. _____28.091_____ Add 1.3; 17.89; and 8.901.

5. _____6.705_____ Subtract 2.895 from 9.6.

6. _____5_____ Write the number of decimal places in the product of 4.59 times .095.

7. _____.9_____ Round off .936 to the nearest tenth.

8. _____.94_____ Round off .936 to the nearest hundredth.

9. _____3.06_____ Write three and six hundredths as a mixed decimal.

10. _____$9.23_____ Find the cost to the nearest cent for 5 gallons of gasoline at $1.845
       9.25   per gallon.

Find the answers. *10 each*

11. $8 \div \frac{2}{3} = $ _12_

12. $\frac{\frac{3}{5}}{\frac{9}{10}} = \frac{2}{3}$

13. $\begin{array}{r} 73.86 \\ 5.932 \\ +16.7 \\ \hline 96.492 \end{array}$

14. $\begin{array}{r} .003 \\ \times \quad .4 \\ \hline .0012 \end{array}$

Name _____ Date _____ Score _____

QUIZ 6   *Basic Mathematics*
Units 2–4 (2.1–4.3)

Write *true* or *false* in each blank. *5 each*

1. ___true___ A ratio compares two quantities by using division.

2. ___false___ The second term in a ratio is the antecedent.

3. ___true___ In a proportion, the product of the means is equal to the product of the extremes.

Find the answers. *7 each*

4. $4\frac{3}{8}$
   $11\frac{1}{4}$
   $+ 8\frac{5}{6}$
   $24\frac{11}{24}$

5. $15\frac{2}{5}$
   $- 9\frac{3}{4}$
   $5\frac{13}{20}$

6. $3\frac{1}{3} \times 2\frac{5}{8} = \underline{8\frac{3}{4}}$

7. $\frac{15}{\frac{3}{4}} = 20$

8. 3.2
   6.5
   $+ 0.9$
   10.6

9. 27.566
   7.59
   18.71
   $+ 9.9$
   63.766

10. 13.1
    $- 7.25$
    5.85

11. 63.72
    $- 6.5$
    57.22

12. 1.2
    $\times .37$
    $.444$

13. $.07$
    $\times .06$
    $.0042$

14. 7.32
    $\times 5.9$
    43.188

15. $3.8\overline{)9.12}$ 2.4

TEST 2   *Basic Mathematics*

Units 2–4

Find the answers. Show all of your work. *3 each (36)*

1. _____ $22\frac{3}{20}$ _____

2. _____ $2\frac{5}{12}$ _____

3. _____ 6 _____

4. _____ $\frac{3}{4}$ _____

5. _____ $4\frac{1}{2}$ _____

6. _____ 3 _____

7. _____ 26.2177 _____

8. _____ 0.475 _____

9. _____ 36.9402 _____

10. _____ $.0155$ _____

11. _____ 6.4 _____

12. _____ 13.59 _____

1. $\begin{array}{r} 5\frac{1}{2} \\ 8\frac{2}{5} \\ + 8\frac{1}{4} \\ \hline \end{array}$

2. $\begin{array}{r} 11\frac{1}{12} \\ - 8\frac{2}{3} \\ \hline \end{array}$

3. $9 \times \frac{2}{3} =$

4. $2\frac{1}{4} \div 3 =$

5. $2\frac{2}{3} \times 1\frac{11}{16} =$

6. $3\frac{3}{5} \div 1\frac{1}{5} =$

7. $\begin{array}{r} 4.12 \\ 0.735 \\ 8.2 \\ + 13.1627 \\ \hline \end{array}$

8. $\begin{array}{r} 8.1 \\ - 7.625 \\ \hline \end{array}$

9. $\begin{array}{r} 5.79 \\ \times 6.38 \\ \hline \end{array}$

10. $\begin{array}{r} 3.1 \\ \times .005 \\ \hline \end{array}$

11. $32\overline{)204.8}$

12. $.7\overline{)9.51}$ (Round to the nearest hundredth.)

Round off 6.9937 as directed in problems 13 to 15. *2 each (6)*

13. _____ 6.994 _____ nearest thousandth

14. _____ 7.0 _____ nearest tenth

15. _____ 6.99 _____ nearest hundredth

Follow the directions. Show all of your work. *2 each (30)*

16. _____$86.82_____ Multiply $8.95 by 9.7 and round off the product to the nearest cent.

17. _____.72_____ Write the greater: .718 or .72.

18. _____.4_____ Write the decimal equivalent of $\frac{2}{5}$.

19. _____$\frac{7}{8}$_____ Write the fraction equivalent of .875.

20. _____.156_____ Divide 1.56 by 10.

21. _____73.2_____ Multiply .0732 by 1,000.

22. _____$\frac{51}{10,000}$_____ Write .0051 as a fraction.

23. _____$\frac{75}{8}$_____ Write $9\frac{3}{8}$ as an improper fraction.

24. _____$.\overline{6}$_____ Write the decimal equivalent of $\frac{2}{3}$.

25. _____.56_____ Divide 5 by 9 and round off to the nearest hundredth.

26. _____1:3_____ Write a ratio in lowest terms comparing 5 games won to 15 games played.

27. _____3; 8_____ Write the extremes in $\frac{3}{4} = \frac{6}{8}$.

28. _____5_____ Write the antecedent in 5:6.

29. _____$\frac{3}{4}$_____ Reduce $\frac{27}{36}$ to lowest terms.

30. _____$.8\overline{3}$_____ Write the decimal equivalent of $\frac{5}{6}$.

Write the missing numbers in the proportions. Show all of your work. *1 each (5)*

31. _____9_____ $\frac{3}{7} = \frac{?}{21}$

32. _____2_____ $\frac{?}{9} = \frac{4}{18}$

33. _____12_____ $\frac{7}{?} = \frac{84}{144}$

34. _____44_____ $\frac{9}{11} = \frac{36}{?}$

35. _____27_____ $\frac{3}{5} = \frac{?}{45}$

Solve the word problems. Show all of your work. *4 each (20)*

36. _____1.694 in._____ In May 3.4 inches of rain were recorded. In June 1.706 inches were recorded. How many more inches did it rain in May than it rained in June?

37. $\frac{232}{4} = \frac{?}{8}$; 464 mi. If Tom Parsons traveled 232 miles in 4 hours, how many miles should he travel in 8 hours at the same rate of speed? Write a proportion and solve.

38. _____$23\frac{1}{4}$ hr._____ On Monday, Lyn Johnson worked for $3\frac{3}{4}$ hours. Tuesday through Thursday, she worked for $4\frac{1}{3}$ hours each day. On Friday, she worked for $6\frac{1}{2}$ hours. How many hours total did she work during the five days?

39. _____16 gal._____ Jeremy Jax says his car averages 32 miles per gallon of gasoline. How many gallons of gas does he need to travel 500 miles? Find the answer to the nearest whole gallon.

40. _____5 bags_____ Megan Shores made $3\frac{1}{3}$ pounds of fudge. She divided it into bags with $\frac{2}{3}$ of a pound in each bag. How many bags of fudge did she have?

Name _____ Date _____ Score _____

QUIZ 7   *Basic Mathematics*

Unit 5 (5.1–5.7)

Express each percent as a decimal. *5 each*

   1. ____.56____ 56%

   2. ____.05____ 5%

   3. ____.005____ $\frac{1}{2}$%

Express each decimal as a percent. *5 each*

   4. ____78%____ .78

   5. ____3%____ .03

Express each fraction as a percent. *5 each*

   6. ____25%____ $\frac{1}{4}$

   7. ____40%____ $\frac{2}{5}$

Find the percentages. *10 each*

8. 10% of 560	9. 25% of 48	10. 5% of 400
56	12	20
11. 14% of 100	12. 4% of 260	13. 50% of 2,000
14	10.4	1,000

QUIZ 8   *Basic Mathematics*

Unit 5 (5.1–5.11)

Follow the directions. *7 each*

1. _____.27_____ Express 27% as a decimal.

2. _____50%_____ Express $\frac{1}{2}$ as a percent.

3. _____56_____ Find 12% more than 50.

4. _____44_____ Find 12% less than 50.

5. _____.05375_____ Express $5\frac{3}{8}$% as a decimal.

6. _____$62\frac{1}{2}$%_____ Find what percent 25 is of 40.

7. _____33%_____ Find what percent 12 is of 36. Find the answer to the nearest whole percent.

8. ___20% increase___ Find the percent of increase from 5 dogs to 6 dogs.

9. ___12% decrease___ Find the percent of decrease from $25 to $22.

10. _____64%_____ Subtract 36% from 100%.

Find the percentages. *10 each*

11. 30% of 200   12. 15% of 80   13. $3\frac{1}{2}$% of 500

    60   12   17.5

QUIZ 9   *Basic Mathematics*

Unit 5 (5.1–5.15)

Follow the directions. *7 each*

1. _____72.5%_____ Subtract 27.5% from 100%.

2. _____.1275_____ Express $12\frac{3}{4}\%$ as a decimal.

3. _____2.25_____ Express 225% as a decimal.

4. _____40%_____ Express $\frac{2}{5}$ as a percent.

5. _____100_____ Find 25% more than 80.

6. _____60_____ Find 25% less than 80.

7. _____$12_____ Find a 20% discount on $60.

8. _____$35_____ Find the sale price if the $50 price is discounted 30%.

9. __25% increase__ Find the percent of increase from $40 to $50.

10. _____$300_____ Find a 5% commission on a sale of $6,000.

Find the answers. *10 each*

11. 38% of 400   12. 45 is what % of 50?   13. 12 is 40% of what number?

    152   90%   30

Name _____ Date _____ Score _____

TEST 3 _____ *Basic Mathematics*

Units 1–5

Find the answers. Show all of your work. *3 each (45)*

1. ____73.251____

2. ____1,987____

3. ____$3\frac{5}{6}$____

4. ____$14\frac{1}{12}$____

5. ____10____

6. ____$6\frac{3}{5}$____

7. ____7.475____

8. ____397.848____

9. ____.003____

10. ____135____

11. ____15____

12. ____100____

13. ____400____

14. ____35.2____

15. ____.5____

1. 6.35
    2.074
    56.35
  + 8.477

2. 6,271
  − 4,284

3. $7\frac{1}{3}$
  − $3\frac{1}{2}$

4. $4\frac{1}{4}$
    $3\frac{1}{3}$
  + $6\frac{1}{2}$

5. $2\frac{2}{3} \times 3\frac{3}{4} =$

6. $9\frac{9}{10} \div 1\frac{1}{2} =$

7. 15.1
  − 7.625

8. 7.26
  × 54.8

9. .05
  × .06

10. 18% of 750

11. $2\frac{1}{2}$% of 600

12. 400% of 25

13. 60 is 15% of what number?

14. $6.7\overline{)235.84}$

15. $3\overline{)1.6}$ (nearest tenth)

Round off 7,894,783.8993 as directed in problems 16 to 18. *1 each (3)*

16.   8,000,000   nearest one million

17.   7,894,783.90   nearest hundredth

18.   7,890,000   nearest ten thousand

Follow the directions. Show all of your work. *2 each (20)*

19. $\frac{5}{6}$ Reduce $\frac{15}{18}$ to lowest terms.

20. $\frac{27}{5}$ Change $5\frac{2}{5}$ to an improper fraction.

21.   63   Write the missing term in $\frac{7}{9} = \frac{?}{81}$.

22.   77%   Subtract 23% from 100%.

23.   .0775   Express $7\frac{3}{4}$% as a decimal.

24.   450%   Express 4.5 as a percent.

25.   3.8   Round 3.763 to the nearest tenth.

26.   25% decrease   Find the percent of decrease from 40 hours to 30 hours.

27. $30   Find the amount of discount if the price of $75 is discounted 40%.

28. $105   Find the sale price if the price of $140 is discounted 25%.

Follow the directions. Show all of your work. *2 each (24)*

29. _____236_____ Find 18% more than 200.

30. _____52.8_____ Find 12% less than 60.

31. _____.8$\overline{3}$_____ Express $\frac{5}{6}$ as a decimal.

32. _36 = 2 × 2 × 3 × 3_ Write the prime factors of 36.

33. _____6_____ Write the greatest common factor of 12 and 18.

34. _____24_____ Write the least common multiple of 6 and 8.

35. _____90_____ Find 15% of 600.

36. _____25%_____ Find what percent 30 is of 120.

37. _____85_____ Find 8$\frac{1}{2}$% of 1,000.

38. _____1,570_____ Multiply 1.57 by 1,000.

39. _____$50_____ Find the gross profit if a dog is bought for $75 and sold for $125.

40. _____$23.90_____ Round off $23.8954 to the nearest cent.

Solve the word problems. Show all of your work. *1 each (5)*

41. _____$30.24_____   Brendon Butterworth bought a present for his mother. He spent
$28 plus 8% sales tax. Find the total cost of the present.

42. _____$1,825_____   Nicole Davis receives a 5% commission on her sales. Last month
she had $36,500 in sales. Find her commission.

43. _____$44,800_____   Mr. Turner earned $40,000 last year. This year he estimates that he
will earn 12% more money. How much does he estimate that he
will earn this year?

44. _____20% decrease_____   Pat Pollix paid $80 for a dress that listed for $100. Find the percent
of decrease. (The percent of decrease is the same as the rate of
discount.)

45. _____20 hr._____   Jay Downs only worked 15 of his scheduled hours last week. If he
worked 75% of his scheduled hours, how many hours was he sched-
uled to work?

Name _____ Date _____ Score _____

QUIZ 10   *Basic Mathematics*

Unit 6 (6.1–6.5)

Write the correct number. *5 each*

1. 1 yd. = __36__ in.   2. 1 mi. = __5,280__ ft.   3. 1 pk. = __8__ qt.

4. 1 m = __100__ cm   5. 1 pt. = __16__ fl. oz.   6. 1 cL = __10__ mL

Follow the directions. *7 each*

7. __21 ft.__ Write the number of feet in 7 yards.

8. __7 ft.__ Write the number of feet in 84 inches.

9. __1,600 L__ Write the number of liters in 1.6 kiloliters.

10. __54 in.__ Write the number of inches in $4\frac{1}{2}$ feet.

11. __$2\frac{1}{2}$ yd.__ Write the number of yards in 90 inches.

12. __8 daL__ Write the number of decaliters in 80 liters.

13. __8 tbsp.__ Write the number of tablespoons in 24 teaspoons.

14. __32 qt.__ Write the number of quarts in 8 gallons.

Mark under the greatest in each row. *5 each*

15. yard	centimeter	mile	meter	kilometer
○	○	●	○	○

16. liter	fluid ounce	tablespoon	quart	pint
●	○	○	○	○

QUIZ 11   *Basic Mathematics*

Unit 6 (6.5–6.9)

Write the correct number. *5 each*

1. 1 lb. = __16__ oz.   2. 1 kg = __1,000__ g   3. 1 century = __100__ yr.

4. 1 yr. = __365__ da.   5. 1 t. = __2,000__ lb.   6. 1 dag = __100__ dg

Follow the directions. *7 each*

7. _____2012_____ Write the next year after 2009 that is a leap year.

8. _____1904_____ Write the next year after 1899 that was a leap year.

9. _____ounce_____ Write the heavier: gram or ounce.

10. _____meter_____ Write the longer: meter or yard.

11. _____liter_____ Write the one that holds more: liter or quart.

12. _____96 oz._____ Write the number of ounces in 6 pounds.

13. _____42 mo._____ Write the number of months in $3\frac{1}{2}$ years.

14. _____1,000 yr._____ Write the number of years in a millennium.

15. _____16 km_____ Convert 10 miles to the nearest whole kilometer. Remember that a mile is longer than a kilometer. Therefore, the number of kilometers will be greater than 10.

16. _____35 lb._____ Convert 16 kilograms to the nearest whole pound. Remember that a kilogram is heavier than a pound. Therefore, the number of pounds will be greater than 16.

QUIZ 12   *Basic Mathematics*

Unit 6 (6.1–6.14)

Write the correct number. *5 each*

1. 1 c. = ___8___ fl. oz.   2. 1 dm = ___100___ mm   3. 1 doz. = ___12___ things

4. 1 hg = ___10___ dag   5. 1 mi. = ___1,760___ yd.   6. 1 km = ___10___ hm

Find the answers. *8 each*

7.   5 yr.   8 mo.
       8 yr.   6 mo.
    + 4 yr.   5 mo.
     1 8 yr.   7 mo.

8.   8 lb.   3 oz.
   − 2 lb.   9 oz.
     5 lb. 10 oz.

9.   3 cm   5 mm
    ×   7
   2 4 cm   5 mm

10.   5 kL   2 hL
     7 kL   5 hL
   + 3 kL   7 hL
   1 6 kL   4 hL

11.   5 yd.   8 in.
   − 2 yd.   2 7 in.
    2 yd.   17 in.

12.   1 wk.   4 da.
   4 ⟌ 6 wk.   2 da.

Follow the directions. *5 each*

13. ___2 decades___ Convert 20 years to decades.

14. ___8 oz.___ Convert 200 grams to ounces. Remember that a gram weighs less than an ounce. Therefore, the number of ounces will be less than 200.

15. ___35 oz.___ Convert 2 pounds, 3 ounces to ounces.

16. ___9 yd.___ Convert 7 yards, 6 feet to yards.

TEST 4   *Basic Mathematics*

Unit 6

Find the answers and simplify. Show all of your work. *3 each (30)*

1. _____24 lb. 13 oz._____

2. _____6 ft. 11 in._____

3. _____26 L 8 dL_____

4. _____3 yr. 8 mo._____

5. _____4 g 7 dg_____

6. _____14 kg 2 hg_____

7. _____2 cm 5 mm_____

8. _____16 gal. 2 qt._____

9. _____2 pk. 5 qt._____

10. _____11 tbsp. 1 tsp._____

1.   8 lb.   9 oz.
      6 lb.   8 oz.
   + 9 lb. 12 oz.

2.   15 ft. 3 in.
   − 8 ft. 4 in.

3.   6 L 7 dL
   ×   4

4. $5 \overline{)18 \text{ yr.} \ \ 4 \text{ mo.}}$

5. $2 \overline{)9 \text{ g} \ \ 4 \text{ dg}}$

6.   6 kg 4 hg
   + 7 kg 8 hg

7.   9 cm 4 mm
   − 6 cm 9 mm

8.   5 gal. 2 qt.
   ×   3

9.   7 pk. 2 qt.
   − 4 pk. 5 qt.

10. $2 \overline{)22 \text{ tbsp.} \ \ 2 \text{ tsp.}}$

Write the greater in each blank. *2 each (10)*

11. _____meter_____ meter or yard

12. _____liter_____ quart or liter

13. _____mile_____ mile or kilometer

14. _____inch_____ centimeter or inch

15. _____kilogram_____ pound or kilogram

Write the correct number in each blank. *2 each (20)*

16. _____100_____ meters = 1 hectometer

17. _____24_____ hours = 1 day

18. _____3_____ teaspoons = 1 tablespoon

19. _____100_____ milliliters = 1 deciliter

20. _____10_____ decigrams = 1 gram

21. _____5,280_____ feet = 1 mile

22. _____1,000_____ centimeters = 1 decameter

23. _____8_____ quarts = 1 peck

24. _____2_____ pints = 1 quart

25. _____10_____ years = 1 decade

Convert. Show all of your work. *2 each (10)*

26. _____72_____ hours = 3 days

27. _____144_____ ounces = 9 pounds

28. _____5_____ kilograms = 5,000 grams

29. _____34,320_____ feet = $6\frac{1}{2}$ miles

30. _____7,000_____ meters = 700 decameters

Convert. Show all of your work. *2 each (10)*

31. _____$4\frac{1}{2}$_____ gallons = 18 quarts

32. _____8_____ pounds = 128 ounces

33. _____.25_____ hectoliter = 25 liters

34. _____1,300_____ years = 13 centuries

35. _____80_____ fluid ounces = 5 pints

Solve the word problems. Show all of your work. *3 each (15)*

36. ___3 hr. 55 min.___ Tyler Thomas practiced his tuba five days last week. He practiced these times: 1 hr. 10 min., 25 min., 30 min., 1 hr. 5 min., and 45 min. How many hours and minutes did he practice last week?

37. ___15 hr. 45 min.___ Last week, Mr. Welch worked 40 hours. This week, due to illness, he only worked 24 hours and 15 minutes. How many more hours and minutes did he work last week than he worked this week?

38. ___6 lb. 8 oz.___ The five babies born on October 15 weighed a total of 32 pounds 8 ounces. What was the average weight of the babies?

39. _____$6\frac{3}{4}$ ft._____ Lance Tolbert is 6 feet, 9 inches tall. Express his height using feet only.

40. _____805 km_____ Denise White traveled 500 miles in one day. How many kilometers did she travel?

QUIZ 13   *Basic Mathematics*

Unit 7 (7.1–7.6)

Write *true* or *false* in each blank. *7 each*

1. ___false___ A depositor should keep his PIN (personal identification number) with his ATM (automatic teller machine) card.

2. ___true___ The balance in a bank account changes each time a deposit or withdrawal is made.

3. ___false___ Interest that is added to an account quarterly is paid six times per year.

4. ___true___ Paying bills by checks or debit card frees a person from having to keep large amounts of cash on hand.

5. ___false___ A full roll of pennies has only 35 pennies.

6. ___false___ The person writing a check should sign his name before he writes anything else on the check.

7. ___false___ If the rate in the simple interest formula is an annual one, time should be given in months.

8. ___true___ A budget can help to eliminate foolish and "spur-of-the-moment" buying.

9. ___true___ Canceled checks are checks that have been processed by the bank.

10. ___false___ The register number identifies a check on the deposit slip.

Use the formula *i = prt* to find the simple interest. *10 each*

11. $p = \$500$ 12. $p = \$9,000$ 13. $p = \$5,000$
    $r = 9\%$ $r = 12\%$ $r = 11\frac{1}{2}\%$
    $t = 1$ yr. $t = 5$ yr. $t = 3$ yr.
    $i = \$45$ $i = \$5,400$ $i = \$1,725$

QUIZ 14   *Basic Mathematics*

Unit 7 (7.5–7.9)

Complete this monthly budget based on a monthly salary of $2,500. *8 each*

    1. _____$300_____ tithe and offerings—12%

    2. _____$675_____ mortgage—27%

    3. _____$225_____ utilities—9%

    4. _____$350_____ food—14%

    5. _____$125_____ medical—5%

Find the simple interest. *10 each*

  6. p = $3,750   7. p = $22,000   8. p = $1,600
     $r = 12\%$ $r = 8\frac{3}{4}\%$ $r = 15\%$
     $t = 2$ yr. $t = 5$ yr. $t = 3$ mo.
     i = $900   *i = $9,625*   *i = $60*

Solve the word problems. *10 each*

    9. _____$100_____ Nate Williams borrowed $500 from a loan company for 12 months. He signed a note to repay the loan at $50 per month. How much interest did he have to pay?

   10. _____$1,103_____ Heather Thompson has a credit line of $3,000 on a department store credit card. Her present balance on the card is $1,897. How much can she charge without exceeding her credit limit?

   11. _____$215_____ Ethan Parker borrowed $1,200 from a loan company at 15% simple interest for 6 months. How much did he have to pay each month on the installment plan?

Name _____ Date _____ Score _____

QUIZ 15   *Basic Mathematics*

Unit 7 (7.1–7.16)

Find the percent budgeted for each based on a monthly salary of $3,200. *6 each*

1. ____12%____ tithe—$384

2. ____27%____ mortgage—$864

3. _____9%____ utilities—$288

4. ____14%____ food—$448

5. _____5%____ medical—$160

Write the correct answer in the blank. *6 each*

6. ____budget____ a plan to spend money

7. ___premium___ an insurance payment

8. __beneficiary__ a person who benefits from a life insurance policy

9. _____tax_____ required money paid to a government

10. ___insurance___ a protection against material loss

Solve the word problems. *10 each*

11. ___$1,964.65___ Melanie Brian had a balance of $1,895 in her checking account before she deposited $347.65 and wrote a check for $278. Find her new balance.

12. ___$1,912.50___ Luke Luckless bought $150,000 of straight life insurance at the rate of $12.75 per thousand dollar unit. What is his yearly premium?

13. _____$132_____ Nicole Donnaldson borrowed $1,200 for 1 year at a rate of 11%. What was the simple interest?

14. _____20%_____ Bobby Buckett's medical insurance paid 80% of a $17,000 surgery charge. What percent did Mr. Buckett have to pay?

TEST 5   *Basic Mathematics*

Unit 7

Choose the correct answer from the list below. *2 each (24)*

actuary	canceled check	installment plan
balance	check	premium
beneficiary	deposit slip	tax
budget	finance charge	transit number

1. _____finance charge_____   the interest charged for the use of the installment plan

2. _____budget_____   a plan used in spending money

3. ____transit number____   the number used to identify a check on the deposit slip

4. _____premium_____   an insurance payment

5. _____actuary_____   a person who makes insurance calculations and predictions

6. _____check_____   an order for a bank to pay money

7. _____tax_____   a required payment for the support of the government

8. _____balance_____   the amount of money in a bank account

9. ____deposit slip____   form used to put money in a bank account

10. ___canceled check___   check cashed by the bank

11. ___installment plan___   buying on time

12. _____beneficiary_____   a person who benefits from an insurance policy

Find the simple interest. Show all of your work. *4 each (16)*

13. _____$100_____ $p = \$1,000;\ r = 10\%;\ t = 1$ yr.

14. _____$360_____ $p = \$1,500;\ r = 12\%;\ t = 2$ yr.

15. _____$60_____ $p = \$800;\ r = 15\%;\ t = 6$ mo.

16. _____$33_____ $p = \$3,600;\ r = 11\%;\ t = 30$ da.

Complete this monthly budget based on a monthly salary of $2,800. Show all of your work. *3 each (15)*

17. ____$308____ tithe and offerings—11%

18. ____$784____ mortgage—28%

19. ____$196____ utilities—7%

20. ____$336____ food—12%

21. ____$252____ medical—9%

Follow the directions. Show all of your work. *4 each (16)*

22. ____$663.28____ Find the total deposit if $567.39 is deposited in checks, $95 in currency, and $.89 in coins.

23. ____$2,615____ Find the new balance if $875 is deposited and $316 is withdrawn from a balance of $2,056.

24. ____$443.34____ A checkbook register began the page with a balance of $600.84. A check was written for $89.50. A deposit was made for $55. Bank charges of $25 were recorded. A check was written for $23, and a check was written for $75. Find the balance after these transactions have been accounted for.

25. ____16%____ Jonathan Sedridge budgeted $40 of his $250 for church activities. What percent of his money did he budget for church activities?

Follow the directions. Show all of your work. *4 each (28)*

26. _____$85_____   Mrs. Patrick bought a vacuum cleaner with a list price of $349. She paid $50 down and the rest in 12 monthly payments of $32 each month. Find the amount of interest she had to pay.

27. _____$1,387.50_____   Find the annual premium for $75,000 in straight life insurance at $18.50 per thousand dollar unit.

28. _____$2,220_____   Raymond Blount pays $185 each month for health insurance. Find the amount he pays in one year.

29. _____$804_____   Dr. Wilson insured his home at the rate of $.67 per $100 per year. The insurance company valued his home at $120,000. Find his cost for one year of homeowner's insurance.

30. _____$719_____   Peter Pepper pays $425 for liability insurance, $216 for collision insurance, and $78 for comprehensive insurance. Find the total cost for his car insurance.

31. _____$50_____   Find the sales tax on a purchase of $625 at the sales tax rate of 8%.

32. _____$6,300_____   Find the amount of income tax on a taxable income of $35,000 at a tax rate of 18%.

QUIZ 16   *Basic Mathematics*

Unit 8 (8.1–8.5)

Find the hours worked. *8 each*

1. ___$5\frac{1}{2}$ hr.___   7:30 A.M. to 1:00 P.M.

2. ___$9\frac{1}{2}$ hr.___   5:15 A.M. to 2:45 P.M.

3. ___$7\frac{1}{2}$ hr.___   3:30 A.M. to 11:00 A.M.

Find the unit price to the nearest tenth of one cent. *8 each*

4. _$.167 or 16.7¢_ 9 ounces for $1.50

5. _$.233 or 23.3¢_ 15 ounces for $3.50

6. _$.313 or 31.3¢_ 4 ounces for $1.25

Find the kilowatt-hours used. *7 each*

7. ___2 kw-hr___   400 watts for 5 hours

8. ___4 kw-hr___   8 kilowatts for 30 minutes

9. ___6 kw-hr___   250 watts for 1 day

Follow the directions. *10 each*

10. ___$600___   Mr. Peterson earns $15 per hour. Find his gross pay for working 40 hours.

11. ___$65.25___   Find the cost of 870 kilowatt-hours of electricity at the rate of 7.5¢ per kilowatt-hour.

12. _95,284 kw-hr_ Write the number of kilowatt-hours recorded on the electric meter.

Name _____ Date _____ Score _____

Unit 8, Review Lessons

Follow the directions. *6 each*

1. _____$50_____ Find the simple interest if the principal is $500, the rate is 10%, and the time is 1 year.

2. _____$425_____ Find the commission if the rate is 5% and the sales are $8,500.

3. _____$\frac{3}{8}$ c._____ Convert $\frac{3}{4}$ cup cocoa in a recipe that serves 10 to one that serves 5.

4. _____$196_____ Find the gross pay for working 20 hours at the rate of $9.80 per hour.

5. _____$113.10_____ Find the cost for 1,300 kilowatt-hours of electricity at the rate of 8.7¢ per kilowatt-hour.

6. _____$.22 or 22¢_____ Find the unit price for 5 ounces at $1.10.

7. _____1 hr. 55 min._____ Subtract 3 hours 20 minutes from 5 hours 15 minutes.

8. _____8 tbsp._____ Convert 24 teaspoons to tablespoons.

9. _____25% decrease_____ Find the percent of decrease from $80 to $60.

10. _____560_____ Multiply 5.6 by 100.

11. _____$56.88_____ Round off $56.8796 to the nearest cent.

12. _____.0025_____ Express $\frac{1}{4}$% as a decimal.

13. _____10_____ Write the missing number in the proportion: $\frac{5}{8} = \frac{}{16}$.

14. _____.8$\overline{3}$_____ Express $\frac{5}{6}$ as a repeating decimal.

15. _____meter_____ Choose the longer: meter or yard.

16. _____.05_____ Choose the greater: .05 or .049.

TEST 6   *Basic Mathematics*

Units 1–8

Find the answers. Show all of your work. *2 each (30)*

1. _____2,321_____

2. _____44,058_____

3. _____83_____

4. _____1.176_____

5. _____.00087_____

6. _____1.5459_____

7. _____$2\frac{7}{8}$_____

8. _____$33\frac{13}{24}$_____

9. _____10_____

10. _____140_____

11. _____50_____

12. _____15%_____

13. _____8 pk. 1 qt._____

14. _____12 lb. 3 oz._____

15. _____3 cm 7 mm_____

1. $\begin{array}{r} 754 \\ 692 \\ +\,875 \\ \hline \end{array}$

2. $\begin{array}{r} 63,842 \\ -\,19,784 \\ \hline \end{array}$

3. $56\overline{)4,648}$

4. $\begin{array}{r} 5.6 \\ \times\,.21 \\ \hline \end{array}$

5. $\begin{array}{r} .29 \\ \times\,.003 \\ \hline \end{array}$

6. $\begin{array}{r} 3.2 \\ -\,1.6541 \\ \hline \end{array}$

7. $\begin{array}{r} 5\frac{1}{8} \\ -\,2\frac{1}{4} \\ \hline \end{array}$

8. $\begin{array}{r} 7\frac{1}{3} \\ 18\frac{5}{6} \\ +\,7\frac{3}{8} \\ \hline \end{array}$

9. $\dfrac{2\frac{7}{9}}{\frac{5}{18}}$

10. 35% of 400

11. 6 is 12% of what number?

12. 48 is what percent of 320?

13. $6\overline{)48\text{ pk. 6 qt.}}$

14. $\begin{array}{r} 2\,\text{lb. 7 oz.} \\ \times\qquad 5 \\ \hline \end{array}$

15. $\begin{array}{r} 7\,\text{cm}\;\;2\,\text{mm} \\ -\,3\,\text{cm}\;\;5\,\text{mm} \\ \hline \end{array}$

Follow the directions. Show all of your work. *2 each (26)*

16. _____.075_____ Write $7\frac{1}{2}\%$ as a decimal.

17. _____$\frac{7}{2}$_____ Change $3\frac{1}{2}$ to an improper fraction.

18. _____.125_____ Write $\frac{1}{8}$ as a decimal.

19. $32 = 2 \times 2 \times 2 \times 2 \times 2$ Write the prime factors of 32.

20. _____4_____ Write the greatest common factor of 8 and 12.

21. _____12_____ Write the least common multiple of 4 and 6.

22. _____83%_____ Subtract 17% from 100%.

23. _____57,000,000_____ Round off 56,894,568 to the nearest one million.

24. _____$6.90_____ Round off $6.8992 to the nearest cent.

25. _____2,342_____ Write the Arabic value of MMCCCXLII.

26. _____552_____ Choose the number that is divisible by 6: 552 or 525.

27. _____.13_____ Choose the greatest: .03; .099; .103; .13; .129.

28. _____396.584_____ Multiply 3.96584 by 100.

Follow the directions. Show all of your work. *2 each (28)*

29. _____.0876_____ Divide 87.6 by 1,000.

30. _____$1,200_____ Find the simple interest if $5,000 is borrowed for 2 years at 12% rate of interest.

31. _____77_____ Complete proportion: $\frac{7}{11} = \frac{}{121}$.

32. ___50% increase___ Find the percent of increase from 12 to 18.

33. _____46_____ Find 15% more than 40.

34. _____8 gal._____ Convert 32 quarts to gallons.

35. _____$15\frac{1}{2}$ lb._____ Convert 15 pounds 8 ounces to pounds.

36. _____2.5 cm_____ Convert 25 millimeters to centimeters.

37. _____mile_____ Choose the longer: kilometer or mile.

38. _____$114.04_____ A checkbook register has a balance of $158. If a deposit of $35 is made and a check for $78.96 is written, find the new balance.

39. ___$.263 or 26.3¢___ Find the unit cost to the nearest tenth of a cent if 8 ounces cost $2.10.

40. _____2.4 kw-hr._____ Find the kilowatt-hours used if 300 watts are used for 8 hours.

41. _____$6\frac{1}{2}$ hr._____ Find the hours worked if a man works from 8:00 A.M. to 2:30 P.M.

42. ___53,942 kw-hr___ Write the number of kilowatt-hours recorded on the electric meter.

Solve the word problems. Show all of your work. *2 each (16)*

43. _____$364_____ The Jenkins family has $2,800 to budget each month. They budget 13% for food. How much do they budget for food?

44. _____$58.50_____ Kristin Harris bought a dress that was on sale for 25% off the regular price of $78. What was the sale price?

45. _____$52.60_____ Victoria Whit used 578 kw-hr of electricity in December. The rate is 9.1¢ per kw-hr. Find the amount of her electric bill.

46. _____$1,080_____ Garrett Brown bought $200,000 of term life insurance at the rate of $5.40 per thousand-dollar unit. How much is the annual premium?

47. _____$206.40_____ Chad Colby earns $8.60 per hour. What is his gross pay for working 24 hours?

48. _____$17.50_____ Bridget earns $5 per hour baby-sitting. If she baby-sits from 5:00 P.M. to 8:30 P.M., how much will she earn?

49. _____$58.50_____ The Foster family used 6,500 cubic feet of natural gas at the rate of $.90 per hundred cubic feet. What is the cost of the natural gas?

50. _____$3.20_____ Megan was charged an 8% sales tax on a $40 pair of shoes. How much was the sales tax?

Name _____ Date _____ Score _____

QUIZ 18   *Basic Mathematics*

Unit 9 (9.1–9.7)

Follow the directions. *10 each*

1. ___24; 39; 56; 64; 71___ Rank these statistics from least to greatest: 56; 24; 71; 64; and 39.

2. _____73_____ Give the range of these statistics: 27; 32; 74; and 100.

3. _____pictograph_____ Name the bar graph that uses picture symbols.

4. _____line graph_____ Name the type of graph that uses plotted points that are connected with a line.

5. _____circle graph_____ Name the type of graph that uses percentages and is sometimes called a pie chart.

6. _____histogram_____ Name the vertical bar graph that deals with frequency.

Answer the questions about the graph. *5 each*

7. _____bar graph_____ What type of graph is pictured?

8. _____horizontal_____ Are the bars vertical or horizontal?

9. _____squirrel_____ Which animal has the shortest average life span?

10. _____cat; fox_____ Which two animals have the same average life span?

11. _____dog_____ Which animal has an average life span of 13 years?

12. _____beaver_____ Which animal has an average life span of 12 years?

13. _____yes_____ Are the statistics ranked?

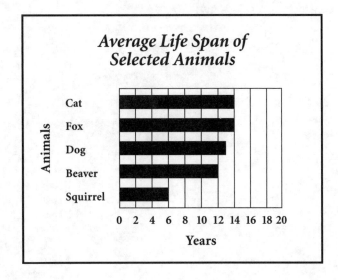

Average Life Span of Selected Animals

Name _____ Date _____ Score _____

QUIZ 19   *Basic Mathematics*

Unit 9 (9.1–9.11)

Answer the questions about the graph. *6 each*

1. _____histogram_____   What type of graph is pictured?

2. _____4_____   How many students made between 60 and 70?

3. _____31_____   How many students does the graph represent?

4. _____no_____   Does the graph show how many students made exactly 77?

5. _____2_____   How many students made between 40 and 50?

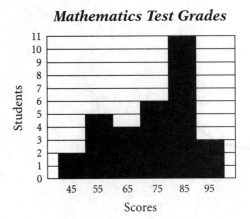

Mathematics Test Grades

Find the mean, median, and mode. *5 each part*

6. _____8—mean_____   12; 10; 9; 4; 10; 8; 3; 5; and 11

_____9—median_____

_____10—mode_____

7. _____52—mean_____   54; 18; 76; 42; 76; and 46

_____50—median_____

_____76—mode_____

Follow the directions. *10 each*

8. _____.571_____   Find the Pct for 12 games won out of 21 games played. Round to the nearest thousandth.

9. _____.556_____   Find the Pct for 10 games won and 8 games lost. Round to the nearest thousandth.

10. _____900 mi._____   If $\frac{1}{4}$ inch equals 50 miles, find the miles represented by $4\frac{1}{2}$ inches.

11. _____11 cm_____   If 1 centimeter represents 40 kilometers, how many centimeters are needed to represent 440 kilometers?

Copyright © mmi Pensacola Christian College • Not to be reproduced.   85

TEST 7   *Basic Mathematics*

Unit 9

Find percentages based upon 400 people in the survey. Show all of your work.

3 each (15)

    1. _____64_____ 16%

    2. _____92_____ 23%

    3. _____36_____ 9%

    4. _____136_____ 34%

    5. _____72_____ 18%

Find the Pct to the nearest thousandth. Show all of your work. *2 each (6)*

    6. _____.600_____ Games won—15; Games played—25

    7. _____.400_____ Games won—10; Games lost—15

    8. _____.500_____ Games won—18; Games lost—18

Find the mean. *3 each (6)*

    9. _____16_____ 14; 25; 18; 14; 9

   10. _____9_____ 9; 11; 8; 7; 10

Find the median. *3 each (6)*

   11. _____42_____ 93; 17; 85; 42; 15; 19; 78

   12. _____10_____ 11; 15; 9; 7; 7; 12

Find the mode. *3 each (6)*

13. _____9_____ 9; 12; 7; 9; 3; 8

14. _____86_____ 97; 86; 85; 93; 86; 88; 91

Name the graph. *3 each (12)*

15. _____circle (or pie)_____

16. _____histogram_____

17. _____pictograph_____

18. _____bar (or column)_____

Answer the questions about this graph. *3 each (15)*

19. _____line_____ What type of graph is it?

20. _____14° F._____ What temperature was recorded for 2 A.M.?

21. _____17° F._____ What temperature was recorded for 9 A.M.?

22. _____5 A.M._____ When was the lowest temperature recorded?

23. _____10 A.M._____ When was the highest temperature recorded?

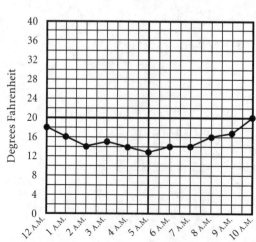

Name _____

Answer the questions about this scale drawing. *2 each (8)*

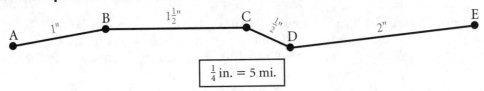

$\frac{1}{4}$ in. = 5 mi.

24. _____ 20 mi. _____ What is the mileage from point A to point B?

25. _____ 10 mi. _____ What is the mileage from point C to point D?

26. _____ 50 mi. _____ What is the mileage from point C to point E?

27. _____ 40 mi. _____ What is the mileage from point B to point D?

Solve the word problems. Show all of your work. *3 each (12)*

28. _74; 85; 91; 93; 97_ Dustin had these grades on his last report slip: 93; 97; 85; 74; and 91. Rank the grades from least to greatest.

29. _____ 326 mi. _____ For the past five days, the Howard family has traveled these miles: 389; 126; 419; 93; and 394. Find the range.

30. _____ $1\frac{1}{8}$ in. _____ If $\frac{1}{4}$ inch represents 50 miles, how many inches are needed to represent 225 miles?

31. _____ 24% _____ Miss Taylor graded 50 English research papers. Twelve of them received a grade of A. Miss Taylor drew a circle graph to display the grades. What percent of the circle graph was devoted to the A papers?

Solve the word problems. Show all of your work. *3 each (12)*

32.   <u>35 students</u>   A histogram showed that 8 students made between 60 and 70, 7 made between 70 and 80, 11 made between 80 and 90, and 9 made between 90 and 100. How many students took the test?

33.   <u>232</u>   Delbert's Deli sold the following sandwiches last week: 145 tuna, 289 turkey, 167 ham, 315 club, and 244 subs. Find the mean number sold.

34.   <u>$4.25</u>   The prices of the sandwiches at Delbert's Deli are as follows: tuna—$4.69; turkey—$3.89; ham—$3.49; club—$4.89; and sub—$4.25. Find the median price.

35.   <u>12 sec.</u>   Six boys on the track team had these times for the 100-meter dash—12 sec., 14 sec., 13 sec., 13.5 sec., 12 sec., and 14.5 sec. Find the mode.

QUIZ 20   *Basic Mathematics*

Unit 10 (10.1–10.5)

Express algebraically. *5 each*

1. $8 + y$ or $y + 8$ 8 plus y

2. $7 + z$ or $z + 7$ 7 more than z

3. $a - 6$ 6 less than a

4. $\frac{15}{m}$ 15 divided by m

5. $12x$ 12 times x

6. $6x - 5$ 5 less than the product of 6 and x

Simplify. *10 each*

7.   14 $2(5 + 6) - 8 =$

8.   19 $4 + 5 \cdot \frac{6}{2} =$

9.   16 $4 \cdot 2(8 - 5) - 8 =$

Solve and check. *10 each* (*Students must apply axioms correctly to receive points for correct answers.*)

10. $x = 9$

$$x + 6 = 15$$
$$x + 6 - 6 = 15 - 6$$
$$x = 9$$
$$9 + 6 = 15$$
$$15 = 15 \checkmark$$

11. $x = 8\frac{3}{4}$

$$x - 3\tfrac{1}{2} = 5\tfrac{1}{4}$$
$$x - 3\tfrac{1}{2} + 3\tfrac{1}{2} = 5\tfrac{1}{4} + 3\tfrac{1}{2}$$
$$x = 8\tfrac{3}{4}$$
$$8\tfrac{3}{4} - 3\tfrac{1}{2} = 5\tfrac{1}{4}$$
$$5\tfrac{1}{4} = 5\tfrac{1}{4} \checkmark$$

12. $x = 8$

$$6x = 48$$
$$\frac{6x}{6} = \frac{48}{6}$$
$$x = 8$$
$$6 \cdot 8 = 48$$
$$48 = 48 \checkmark$$

13. $x = 6$

$$\tfrac{2}{3}x = 4$$
$$\tfrac{3}{2} \cdot \tfrac{2}{3}x = 4 \cdot \tfrac{3}{2}$$
$$x = 6$$
$$\tfrac{2}{3} \cdot 6 = 4$$
$$4 = 4 \checkmark$$

Name _____ Date _____ Score _____

QUIZ 21   *Basic Mathematics*

Unit 10 (10.1–10.9)

Write an equation and solve. *5 each part*

1. $\underline{\quad 2n = 44 \quad}$ Twice a certain number is 44. What is the number?
   $\underline{\quad n = 22 \quad}$

2. $\underline{\quad n + 8 = 23 \quad}$ The sum of a certain number and 8 is 23. What is the number?
   $\underline{\quad n = 15 \quad}$

3. $\underline{\quad 2n - 3 = 5 \quad}$ Three less than two times a number is 5. What is the number?
   $\underline{\quad n = 4 \quad}$

Find the values of *A* in *A = 3x* when *x* equals the given amount. *5 each*

4. $\underline{\quad A = 6 \quad}$ $x = 2$

5. $\underline{\quad A = 24 \quad}$ $x = 8$

6. $\underline{\quad A = 1 \quad}$ $x = \frac{1}{3}$

Write the greater in each blank. *5 each*

7. $\underline{\quad 1 \quad}$ –3 or 1

8. $\underline{\quad 0 \quad}$ 0 or –4

9. $\underline{\quad -6 \quad}$ –6 or –60

Follow the directions. *10 each*

10. $\underline{\quad 5 \quad}$ Write the absolute value of –5.

11. $\underline{\quad x = 4 \quad}$ Solve $4x = 16$ for x.

12. $\underline{\quad mn \quad}$ Express the product of m and n algebraically.

13. $\underline{\quad 0 \quad}$ Write the value of –3 plus 3. (–3 and 3 are inverses.)

QUIZ 22   *Basic Mathematics*

Unit 10 (10.1–10.15)

Find the answers. *8 each*

1. ___−12___   1. −8 + (−4) =   2. 16 + (−9) =

2. ___7___

3. ___11___   3. 5 − (−6) =   4. −8 − (−2) =

4. ___−6___

5. ___−30___   5. 5(−6) =   6. −4(−8) =

6. ___32___

7. ___−5___   7. $\frac{-20}{4}$ =   8. 3^4 =

8. ___81___

Write an equation and solve. *6 each part*

9. ___$3n + 9 = 21$___   The sum of 9 and three times a number is 21. What is the number?
        $n = 4$

10. ___$\frac{2}{3}n = 10$___   Two thirds of a number is 10. What is the number?
        $n = 15$

11. ___$5n = 40$___   Five times a number is 40. What is the number?
        $n = 8$

TEST 8 _____ *Basic Mathematics*

Unit 10

Express algebraically. *2 each (10)*

1. ___5 + x or x + 5___   5 more than x

2. _____$n - 8$_____   8 less than n

3. _2 + 4m or 4m + 2_   2 more than the product of 4 times m

4. _____$x^2 - y^3$_____ x squared minus y cubed

5. _____$\sqrt{s}$_____   the square root of s

Find the values of *T* in *T* = 3x + 2 when *x* equals the given amounts. *2 each (6)*

6. ___$T = 5$___ $x = 1$

7. ___$T = 3$___ $x = \frac{1}{3}$

8. ___$T = 14$___ $x = 4$

Simplify. *2 each (18)*

9. ___27___ $4(3 + 6) - 9 =$

10. ___26___ $5 + 3 \cdot (15 - 8) =$

11. ___$\frac{3}{2}$ or $1\frac{1}{2}$___ $\dfrac{12 - 2 \cdot 3}{4} =$

12. ___216___ 6^3

13. ___16___ 2^4

14. ___64___ 8^2

15. ___8___ $\sqrt{64}$

16. ___10___ $\sqrt{100}$

17. ___5___ $\sqrt{25}$

Solve and check the equations. Show all of your work. *3 each (18)*

18. $x = 6$ $x + 4 = \frac{20}{2}$

19. $x = 13$ $x - 7 = 3 \cdot 2$

20. $x = 4$ $5x = 20$

21. $x = 12$ $\frac{2}{3}x = 8$

22. $x = 16$ $\frac{x}{4} + 3 = 7$

23. $x = 3$ $3x - 6 = \frac{12}{4}$

Find the answers. Show all of your work. *2 each (24)*

24.   13 $19 + (-6) =$

25.   −9 $-5 + (-4) =$

26.   21 $12 - (-9) =$

27.   −14 $(-6) - (+8) =$

28.   −30 $6(-5) =$

29.   32 $-8(-4) =$

30.   9 $14 - (+5) =$

31.   6 $\frac{-36}{-6}$

32.   −8 $\frac{-64}{8}$

33.   14 $\frac{-12}{-2} - (-8) =$

34.   0 $8 + (-8) =$

35.   −5 $5 - 3 - 2 - 4 - 1 =$

Find the square roots by the factoring method or the extracting method. Show all of your work. *2 each (4)*

36. _____24_____   36. $\sqrt{576}$ 37. $\sqrt{2,916}$

37. _____54_____

Write *true* or *false* in each blank. *1 each (11)*

38. _____true_____ $5^1 = 5$

39. _____false_____ $5^0 = 0$

40. _____true_____   Order of operations says to simplify within parentheses first.

41. _____true_____   The division axiom states that both sides of an equation can be divided by the same number, except 0, without changing the value of the equation.

42. _____false_____   The algebraic expression xy has two terms.

43. _____true_____   A number and a variable written side by side as in $3n$ indicate multiplication.

44. _____true_____   Division in algebra is usually shown using the fraction bar.

45. _____false_____   The absolute value of -8 is -8.

46. _____true_____ $P = 2l + 2w$ is an example of a formula.

47. _____false_____ -9 is greater than 0.

48. _____false_____   The sum of two negative numbers is a positive number.

Write an equation and solve. Show all of your work. *2 each (8)*

49. ___$3n = 33$___   Three times a number is 33. What is the number?
       $n = 11$

50. ___$2n - 4 = 20$___   Four less than twice a number is 20. What is the number?
       $n = 12$

Name _____ Date _____ Score _____

Unit 11 (11.1–11.4)

Write *true* or *false* in each blank. *5 each*

1. ____true____ Imaginary lines that are drawn from the North Pole to the South Pole and measure distances east to west are called meridians of longitude.

2. ____false____ Geographers choose the International Date Line to be the "starting point" for measuring longitude.

3. ____false____ The sun seems to move 90° east to west every hour.

4. ____true____ All places on the same meridian of longitude have the same time according to the sun.

5. ____true____ The earth has been divided into twenty-four time zones.

6. ____false____ The United States has seven time zones.

7. ____false____ All of the states in the United States observe daylight-saving time from November to March.

8. ____true____ The imaginary lines that run east and west around the globe are called the parallels of latitude.

9. ____false____ The distance between each degree of latitude is approximately 110 miles.

10. ____true____ The equator is 0° latitude.

Write the correct time. Use A.M. or P.M. in the answer. *7 each*

11. ____5:30 P.M.____ If it is 6:30 P.M. ET, what time is it in the Central Zone?

12. ____10:55 P.M.____ If it is 12:55 A.M. CT, what time is it in the Pacific Zone?

13. ____5:45 P.M.____ If it is 3:45 P.M. MT, what time is it in the Eastern Zone?

14. ____1:00 P.M.____ If it is noon PT, what time is it in the Mountain Zone?

Find the approximate miles. *7 each*

15. ____1,035 mi.____ From the equator to 15° latitude

16. ____690 mi.____ From 15° North latitude to 25° North latitude

17. ____2,760 mi.____ From 15° North latitude to 25° South latitude

QUIZ 24   *Basic Mathematics*

Unit 11 (11.1–11.9)

Write the correct temperatures on the Fahrenheit scale. *4 each*

1. _____98.6°_____ normal body temperature

2. _____212°_____ boiling point of water

3. _____32°_____ freezing point of water

Write the correct temperatures on the Celsius scale. *4 each*

4. _____37°_____ normal body temperature

5. _____100°_____ boiling point of water

6. _____0°_____ freezing point of water

Write the correct temperature zone. *4 each*

7. _____frigid_____ $+66\frac{1}{2}°$ latitude to $+90°$ latitude and $-66\frac{1}{2}°$ latitude to $-90°$ latitude—coldest climate on earth

8. _____temperate_____ $+23\frac{1}{2}°$ latitude to $66\frac{1}{2}°$ latitude and $-23\frac{1}{2}°$ latitude to $-66\frac{1}{2}°$ latitude—wide range of temperatures and has seasons

9. _____torrid_____ $+23\frac{1}{2}°$ latitude to $-23\frac{1}{2}°$ latitude—warm all year

Write the time for each zone if it is 11:15 A.M. Central Time. Use A.M. or P.M. in the answer. *10 each*

10. _____10:15 A.M._____ Mountain Zone

11. _____12:15 P.M._____ Eastern Zone

12. _____9:15 A.M._____ Pacific Zone

Convert to the other scale. *10 each*

13. _____77 °F._____ 25 °C

14. _____−40 °C_____ −40 °F.

15. _____30 °C_____ 86 °F.

Name _____ Date _____ Score _____

TEST 9   *Basic Mathematics*
Units 9–11

Write the time for each zone if it is 10:30 P.M. in the Mountain Zone. Use A.M. or P.M. in the answer. *2 each (6)*

1. ___12:30 A.M.___ Eastern Zone

2. ___9:30 P.M.___ Pacific Zone

3. ___11:30 P.M.___ Central Zone

Find the approximate miles from the equator. *2 each (6)*

4. ___828 mi.___ 12° North latitude

5. ___2,967 mi.___ 43° South latitude

6. ___690 mi.___ –10° latitude

Convert these temperatures to the nearest whole degree. *3 each (9)*

7. ___68 °F.___ 20 °C = ____ °F.

8. ___40 °C___ 104 °F. = ____ °C

9. ___46 °F.___ 8 °C = ____ °F.

Find the drop in temperature to the nearest whole degree from sea level to the top of the mountain. *2 each (4)*

10. ___63°___ Mt. Toro—20,932 feet

11. ___42°___ Mt. San Luis—14,014 feet

Follow the directions. Show all of your work. *2 each (30)*

12. _____$x - 7$_____   Express 7 less than x algebraically.

13. _____2_____   Write the number of terms in $5x + 3y$.

14. _____12_____   Write the absolute value of –12.

15. _____8_____   Write the square root of 64.

16. _____25_____   Write the square of 5.

17. _____23_____   Write the mean of 24; 27; 19; 26; 19; 25; and 21.

18. _____24_____   Write the median of 24; 27; 19; 26; 19; 25; and 21.

19. _____19_____   Write the mode of 24; 27; 19; 26; 19; 25; and 21.

20. _____8_____   Write the range of 24; 27; 19; 26; 19; 25; and 21.

21. _____5 in._____   Write the number of inches needed to represent 500 miles if $\frac{1}{4}$ in. = 25 miles.

22. _____.444_____   Find the Pct (percentage of total) if the team won 12 games and lost 15 games. Find the Pct to the nearest thousandth.

23. _____$C = 13$____   Find the value of C in $C = 3x - 2$ if $x = 5$.

24. _____1_____   Write the value of 5^0.

25. _____23_____   Simplify $7 + 2 \cdot (17 - 9)$.

26. _____32_____   Find the square root of 1,024 using either the factoring or extracting method.

Find the answers. Show all of your work. *2 each (12)*

27. _____−16_____ −12 + (−4) =

28. _____−2_____ −7 − (−5) =

29. _____−14_____ − 8 − 6 =

30. _____−35_____ 7(−5) =

31. _____5_____ $\frac{-10}{-2}$ =

32. _____125_____ 5^3 =

Solve and check the equations. Show all of your work. *3 each (9)*

33. _____$x = 4$_____ $4x = 7 + 9$

34. _____$x = 16$_____ $\frac{3}{4}x = 12$

35. _____$x = 6$_____ $2x − 8 = 4$

Write an equation and solve. Show all of your work. *2 each part (8)*

36. _____$2n = 56$_____ Two times a number is 56. What is the number?
         $n = 28$

37. _____$3n − 3 = 12$_____ Three less than three times a number is 12. What is the number?
         $n = 5$

Solve the word problems. Show all of your work. *3 each (15)*

38. _____218 °C_____   Kaitlin's recipe says to bake a pie at 425 °F. To the nearest whole degree, what temperature Celsius should she bake the pie?

39. _____4:00 A.M._____   Mark Pryor, who lives in the Eastern Time Zone, placed a phone call at 7:00 A.M. to his uncle, who lives in the Pacific Time Zone. What time was it in the Pacific Zone when he called?

40. _____500 mi._____   Ted and Cara Nelson are missionaries near the equator. Recently they traveled directly up from –2° South latitude to 5° North latitude. How many miles to the nearest hundred miles did they travel?

41. ___$\frac{1}{4}$; 1; 1$\frac{1}{2}$; 2; 3; 5___   Jeremy worked on his science project these hours last week: 3; 2; 1$\frac{1}{2}$; $\frac{1}{4}$; 1; and 5. Rank the hours from least to greatest.

42. _____30%_____   Of the 30 students who took the last math test, 9 of them made greater than 94. In a circle graph that represents the grades, what percent of it would be devoted to the grades greater than 94?

Unit 12 (12.1–12.6)

Name the geometric symbol. *5 each*

1. _____angle_____ two rays that share a common endpoint

2. __perpendicular lines__ intersecting lines that form four right angles

3. ____parallel lines____ lines that never intersect

4. ____line segment____ a group of points having two endpoints

Name the geometric plane shape. *5 each*

5. ____quadrilateral____ a four-sided polygon

6. _____square_____ a rectangle having four congruent sides

7. _____octagon_____ an eight-sided polygon

8. _____trapezoid_____ a quadrilateral having only two sides that are parallel

Write the formulas. *5 each*

9. $P = 2l + 2w$ perimeter of a rectangle

10. $P = 4s$ perimeter of a square

11. $P = 2l + 2w$ perimeter of a parallelogram

12. $A = s^2$ area of a square

13. $A = lw$ area of a rectangle

14. $A = bh$ area of a parallelogram

Find the areas. *10 each*

15. ___16 sq. ft.___ square—side = 4 ft.

16. ____396 m²____ rectangle—length = 22 m and width = 18 m

17. $13\frac{3}{4}$ sq. ft. parallelogram—base = $5\frac{1}{2}$ ft. and height = $2\frac{1}{2}$ ft.

Name _____ Date _____ Score _____

QUIZ 26   *Basic Mathematics*

Unit 12 (12.7–12.11)

Follow the directions. *7 each*

1. _____ $A = \frac{1}{2}bh$ _____ Write the formula for the area of a triangle.

2. _____ $A = \frac{h(b_1 + b_2)}{2}$ _____ Write the formula for the area of a trapezoid.

3. _____ right angle _____ Write the type of angle that contains 90°.

4. _____ acute angle _____ Write the type of angle that contains less than 90°.

5. _____ 180° _____ Write the number of degrees in a triangle.

6. _____ isosceles _____ Write the type of triangle that has only two congruent sides.

7. _____ 75° _____ Write the number of degrees in the third angle if the other two angles have 25° and 80°.

8. _____ protractor _____ Write the name of the instrument that is used to measure the number of degrees in an angle.

9. _____ 4 _____ Write the number of right angles in a square.

10. _____ 45 in. _____ One side of an equilateral triangle is 15 in. Find the perimeter of the triangle.

Measure the number of degrees to the nearest five degrees. *10 each*

11. _____ 60° _____

12. _____ 90° _____

13. _____ 45° _____

11.
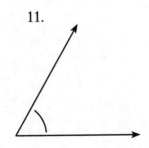

12.
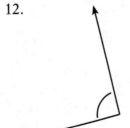

13.
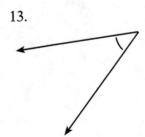

QUIZ 27 *Basic Mathematics*

Unit 12 (12.1–12.18)

Write the area formulas. *5 each*

1. _____$A = s^2$_____ square

2. _____$A = \frac{1}{2}bh$_____ triangle

3. _____$A = \frac{h(b_1 + b_2)}{2}$_____ trapezoid

4. _____$A = bh$_____ parallelogram

5. _____$A = lw$ or bh_____ rectangle

Find the perimeter. *10 each*

6. _____17 ft._____ square—$s = 4\frac{1}{4}$ ft.

7. _____31.4 m_____ rectangle—$l = 8.2$ m; $w = 7.5$ m

Find the circumference. *10 each*

8. _____31.4 ft._____ $r = 5$ ft.

9. _____23.55 cm_____ $d = 7.5$ cm

Find the area. *10 each*

10. _____63 sq. yd._____ trapezoid—$b^1 = 8$ yd.; $b^2 = 6$ yd.; $h = 9$ yd.

11. _____494 sq. ft._____ parallelogram—$b = 26$ ft.; $h = 19$ ft.

12. _____$12\frac{1}{4}$ sq. ft._____ square—$s = 3\frac{1}{2}$ ft.

TEST 10   *Basic Mathematics*

Unit 12

Write the formulas. *2 each (16)*

1. _____ $A = \frac{1}{2}bh$ _____ area of a triangle

2. _____ $P = 4s$ _____ perimeter of a square

3. _____ $C = 2\pi r$ _____ circumference of a circle using the radius

4. _____ $P = 2l + 2w$ _____ perimeter of a rectangle

5. _____ $A = \pi r^2$ _____ area of a circle

6. _____ $A = \frac{h(b_1 + b_2)}{2}$ _____ area of a trapezoid

7. _____ $A = s \cdot s$ or $A = s^2$ _____ area of a square

8. _____ $A = bh$ _____ area of a parallelogram

Write the type of angle. *1 each (4)*

9. _____ right _____ 90°

10. _____ acute _____ less than 90°

11. _____ obtuse _____ more than 90° but less than 180°

12. _____ straight _____ 180°

Write the type of triangle. *1 each (3)*

13. _____ equilateral _____ three congruent sides

14. _____ isosceles _____ only two congruent sides

15. _____ right _____ one right angle

Follow the directions. *2 each (8)*

16. _____ 180° _____ Write the number of degrees in a triangle.

17. _____ compass _____ Write the name of the instrument that is used to draw circles.

18. _____ 6 cm _____ Write the length of the radius in a circle if the diameter is 12 cm.

19. _____ hexagon _____ Write the name of the polygon that has six sides.

Find the perimeter. Show all of your work. *3 each (9)*

20.   __200 cm__   square—$s = 50$ cm

21.   __33 ft.__   rectangle—$l = 9\frac{1}{2}$ ft.; $w = 7$ ft.

22.   __146 yd.__   parallelogram—$l = 38$ yd.; $w = 35$ yd.

Find the area. Show all of your work. *3 each (21)*

23.   __50.24 cm²__   circle—$r = 4$ cm

24.   __183.92 m²__   rectangle—$l = 15.2$ m; $w = 12.1$ m

25.   __24 sq. ft.__   triangle—$b = 8$ ft.; $h = 6$ ft.

26.   __625 sq. ft.__   square—$s = 25$ ft.

27.   __54 sq. in.__   trapezoid—$b^1 = 10$ in.; $b^2 = 8$ in.; $h = 6$ in.

28.   __360 sq. ft.__   parallelogram—$b = 20$ ft.; $h = 18$ ft.

29.   __314 m²__   circle—$r = 10$ m

Find the circumference. *3 each (6)*

30. ___25.12 in.___   *d* = 8 in.

31. ___62.8 m___   *r* = 10 m

Measure the number of degrees in each angle. *3 each (6)*

32. ___105°___   32.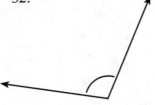

33. ___70°___   33.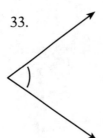

Draw angles with these degrees. Bisect the angle in number 35. *2 each part (6)*

34. 95°   34.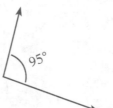

35. 60°   35.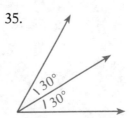

Find the number of degrees in the third angle of the triangle. *2 each (6)*

36. ___78°___   80°; 22°

37. ___61°___   55°; 64°

38. ___60°___   90°; 30°

Write an equation and solve. Show all of your work. *2 each part (12)*

39. ___$x + 2x = 90$___   One angle is twice another angle. The sum of the angles is 90°.
   ___30°, 60°___   How many degrees are in each angle?

40. ___$x + x + 10 = 90$___   One angle has 10° more than another angle. The sum of the
   ___40°, 50°___   angles is 90°. How many degrees are in each angle?

Identify the solid geometric shapes. *8 each*

1. ___square pyramid___

2. ___cylinder___

3. ___rectangular solid___

4. ___cube___

Write the formulas. *6 each*

5. ___$A = lw$ or bh___   area of a rectangle

6. ___$SA = 2lw + 2wh + 2lh$___ surface area of a rectangular solid

7. ___$A = s^2$___   area of a square

8. ___$SA = 6e^2$ or $6s^2$___ surface area of a cube

9. ___$A = \frac{1}{2}bh$___   area of a triangle

10. ___$SA = 4(\frac{1}{2}bh) + b^2$___ surface area of a square pyramid

11. ___$A = \pi r^2$___   area of a circle

12. ___$SA = 2\pi rh + 2\pi r^2$___ surface area of a cylinder

Follow the directions. *10 each*

13. ___216 sq. in.___   Find the surface area of a cube with an edge of 6 in.

14. ___376 sq. ft.___   Find the surface area of a rectangular solid that is 10 ft. long, 8 ft. wide, and 6 ft. high.

QUIZ 29

Basic Mathematics

Unit 13

Write *true* or *false* in each blank. *5 each*

1. ____true____ A cube is an example of a solid shape.

2. ____false____ A rectangular prism is an example of a plane shape.

3. ____true____ Volume is found in cubic units.

4. ____true____ A ball is an example of a sphere.

5. ____true____ The four sides of a square pyramid are in the shape of triangles.

6. ____false____ The two bases of a cylinder are in the shape of squares.

7. ____false____ The lateral surface area of a rectangular solid is found by multiplying the area of one face by 6.

8. ____true____ One cubic foot equals 1,728 cubic inches.

Write the formulas. *6 each*

9. $SA = 2lw + 2wh + 2lh$ surface area of a rectangular solid

10. $SA = 6e^2$ surface area of a cube

11. $SA = 2\pi rh + 2\pi r^2$ surface area of a cylinder

12. $SA = 4(\frac{1}{2}bh) + b^2$ surface area of a square pyramid

13. $V = lwh$ volume of a rectangular solid

14. $V = e^3$ volume of a cube

15. $V = \frac{1}{3}lwh$ volume of a square pyramid

16. $V = \pi r^2 h$ volume of a cylinder

17. $V = \frac{1}{3}\pi r^2 h$ volume of a cone

Name _____ Date _____ Score _____

Write the ratios. *6 each*

1. _____ $S = \frac{o}{h}$ _____ sine

2. _____ $t = \frac{o}{a}$ _____ tangent

3. _____ $c = \frac{a}{h}$ _____ cosine

Write the formulas. *8 each*

4. _____ $c^2 = a^2 + b^2$ _____ Pythagorean rule

5. _____ $V = e^3$ _____ volume of a cube

6. _____ $SA = 2lw + 2wh + 2lh$ _____ surface area of a rectangular solid

7. _____ $V = \frac{1}{3}lwh$ _____ volume of a square pyramid

8. _____ $V = \frac{1}{3}\pi r^2 h$ _____ volume of a cone

Follow the directions. *10 each*

9. _____ 5 m _____ Find the length of the hypotenuse if the legs are 3 m and 4 m.

10. _____ 8 m _____ Find the length of one leg if the hypotenuse is 10 m and the other leg is 6 m.

11. _____ 210 cu. ft. _____ Find the volume of a rectangular solid that is 7 ft. long, 6 ft. wide, and 5 ft. high.

12. _____ 96 sq. in. _____ Find the surface area of a cube that is 4 in. on each edge.

TEST 11

Units 13–14

Identify. *3 each (15)*

1. _____cube_____

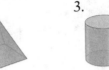

2. __square pyramid__

3. ____cylinder____

4. ____sphere____

5. _____cone_____

Write the formulas. *2 each (18)*

6. _____$V = lwh$_____ volume of a rectangular solid

7. ____$c^2 = a^2 + b^2$____ Pythagorean rule

8. _____$SA = 6e^2$_____ surface area of a cube

9. _____$V = e^3$_____ volume of a cube

10. _____$V = \frac{1}{3}lwh$_____ volume of a square pyramid

11. _____$V = \pi r^2 h$_____ volume of a cylinder

12. _____$A = \pi r^2$_____ area of a circle

13. ___$A = lw \text{ or } bh$___ area of a rectangle

14. _____$V = \frac{1}{3}\pi r^2 h$_____ volume of a cone

Trigonometric Ratios

Measure of angle	sin	cos	tan	Measure of angle	sin	cos	tan
1°	.017	1.000	.017	46°	.719	.695	1.036
2°	.035	.999	.035	47°	.731	.682	1.072
3°	.052	.999	.052	48°	.743	.669	1.111
4°	.070	.998	.070	49°	.755	.656	1.150
5°	.087	.996	.087	50°	.766	.643	1.192
6°	.105	.995	.105	51°	.777	.629	1.235
7°	.122	.993	.123	52°	.788	.616	1.280
8°	.139	.990	.141	53°	.799	.602	1.327
9°	.156	.988	.158	54°	.809	.588	1.376
10°	.174	.985	.176	55°	.819	.574	1.428
11°	.191	.982	.194	56°	.829	.559	1.483
12°	.208	.978	.213	57°	.839	.545	1.540
13°	.225	.974	.231	58°	.848	.530	1.600
14°	.242	.970	.249	59°	.857	.515	1.664
15°	.259	.966	.268	60°	.866	.500	1.732
16°	.276	.961	.287	61°	.875	.485	1.804
17°	.292	.956	.306	62°	.883	.469	1.881
18°	.309	.951	.325	63°	.891	.454	1.863
19°	.326	.946	.344	64°	.899	.438	2.050
20°	.342	.940	.364	65°	.906	.423	2.145
21°	.358	.934	.384	66°	.914	.407	2.246
22°	.375	.927	.404	67°	.921	.391	2.356
23°	.391	.921	.424	68°	.927	.375	2.475
24°	.407	.914	.445	69°	.934	.358	2.605
25°	.423	.906	.466	70°	.940	.342	2.748
26°	.438	.899	.488	71°	.946	.326	2.904
27°	.454	.891	.510	72°	.951	.309	3.078
28°	.469	.883	.532	73°	.956	.292	3.271
29°	.485	.875	.554	74°	.961	.276	3.487
30°	.500	.866	.577	75°	.966	.259	3.732
31°	.515	.857	.601	76°	.970	.242	4.011
32°	.530	.848	.625	77°	.974	.225	4.331
33°	.545	.839	.649	78°	.978	.208	4.705
34°	.559	.829	.675	79°	.982	.191	5.145
35°	.574	.819	.700	80°	.985	.174	5.671
36°	.588	.809	.727	81°	.988	.156	6.314
37°	.602	.799	.754	82°	.990	.139	7.115
38°	.616	.788	.781	83°	.993	.122	8.144
39°	.629	.777	.810	84°	.995	.105	9.514
40°	.643	.766	.839	85°	.996	.087	11.430
41°	.656	.755	.869	86°	.998	.070	14.301
42°	.669	.743	.900	87°	.999	.052	19.081
43°	.682	.731	.933	88°	.999	.035	28.636
44°	.695	.719	.966	89°	1.000	.017	57.290
45°	.707	.707	1.000				

Find the volume. Show all of your work. *3 each (21)*

15. ___125 cm³___   cube—*e* = 5 cm

16. ___504 cu. ft.___   rectangular solid—*l* = 9 ft.; *w* = 8 ft.; *h* = 7 ft.

17. ___141.3 cm³___   cylinder—*r* = 3 cm; *h* = 5 cm

18. ___300 cm³___   square pyramid—*l* = 10 cm; *w* = 10 cm; *h* = 9 cm

19. ___78.5 cu. in.___   cone—*r* = 5 in; *h* = 3 in.

20. ___$33\frac{3}{4}$ cu. ft.___   rectangular solid—*l* = $4\frac{1}{2}$ ft.; *w* = 3 ft.; *h* = $2\frac{1}{2}$ ft.

21. _1,728 cu. yd._ cube—*e* = 12 yd.

Find the surface area. Show all of your work. *3 each (6)*

22. ___54 cm²___   cube—*e* = 3 cm

23. ___40 sq. ft.___   square pyramid—*b* = 4 ft.; *h* = 3 ft.

Find the length of the hypotenuse and then find the sine, cosine, and tangent for ∠ A to the nearest thousandth. *3 each (12)*

24. _____5 m_____ hypotenuse

25. _____.800_____ sine ∠ A

26. _____.600_____ cosine ∠ A

27. _____1.333_____ tangent ∠ A

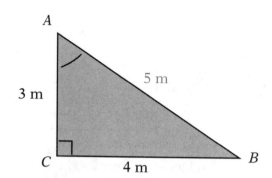

Use the table of trigonometric ratios on page 2 of this test to complete the table.

1 each (15)

	Angle	Sine	Cosine	Tangent
28.	45°	.707	.707	1.000
29.	36°	.588	.809	.727
30.	87°	.999	.052	19.081
31.	12°	.208	.978	.213
32.	25°	.423	.906	.466

Solve the word problems. Show all of your work. *4 each part (12)*

33. ___480 cu. ft.___ Find the volume of a storage room that is 8 feet long, 6 feet wide, and 10 feet high. The room is in the shape of a rectangular solid.

34. ___(A) 384 cm²___ A cube has an edge that is 8 centimeters. Find its (A) surface area and
    ___(B) 512 cm³___ (B) volume.

Name _____ Date _____ Score _____

Unit 15 (15.1–15.3)

Simplify. *8 each*

1. ____18____ –3(–6) =

2. ____2____ – 8 – (–10) =

3. ____–56____ –7(8) =

4. ____12____ 3(2²) =

5. ____12____ 4 + 2³ =

6. ____16____ 5² – 3² =

7. ____22____ 4 + 3²(7 – 5) =

Evaluate. *7 each*

8. ____12.56____ πr^2 if $r = 2$

9. ____252____ *lwh* if $l = 9$; $w = 7$; and $h = 4$

10. ____22____ $y^2 + 2x$ if $y = 4$ and $x = 3$

Use the distributive principle to simplify. *7 each*

11. ____6 + 2x____ 2(3 + x)

12. ____5a – 5b____ 5(a – b)

13. ____4m + 28____ 4(m + 7)

QUIZ 32   *Basic Mathematics*

Unit 15 (15.4–15.6)

Classify as a monomial, binomial, or trinomial. *7 each*

1. __binomial__ $4a + 2b$

2. __monomial__ $6abcxyz$

3. __trinomial__ $x + y - z$

4. __monomial__ $\frac{3}{4}ax$

Write *like* or *unlike* beside each pair of terms. *7 each*

5. ____like____ $9a; 7a$

6. ___unlike___ $4a; 4a^2$

7. ____like____ $-4x; 4x$

Simplify the polynomials by combining like terms. *10 each*

8. ____$12x$____ $3x + 5x + 4x$

9. _____$3x$_____ $9x - 5x - x$

10. __$9a + 3b$__ $7a + 9b - 6b + 2a$

Solve and check. *10 each*

11. ___$x = 4$___ $4x + 2x = 24$

12. ___$x = 2$___ $9x - 3x = 12$

QUIZ 33   *Basic Mathematics*

Unit 15

Simplify.   *10 each*

1. _____−17_____   −6 + (−8) + (−3) =

2. _____3x + 6_____   3(x + 2) =

3. _____6x_____   4x + 2x =

4. _____0_____   9y − 8y − y =

5. _____7a + 2b_____   2(a + b) + 5a =

Solve and check.   *10 each*

6. _____x = 3_____   6 = 2x

7. _____x = 12_____ $\frac{1}{3}x + \frac{1}{4}x = 7$

8. _____x = 5_____   9x − 7x = 10

9. _____x = 5_____   5x + 5 = 4x + 10

10. _____x = 2_____   3(x + 2) = 12

Name _____ Date _____ Score _____

Review

Follow the directions. *5 each*

1. ___.015___ Express $1\frac{1}{2}\%$ as a decimal.

2. ___$\frac{23}{8}$___ Change $2\frac{7}{8}$ to an improper fraction.

3. ___70___ Find $3\frac{1}{2}\%$ of 2,000.

4. ___$56.90___ Round off $56.8953 to the nearest cent.

5. ___4.586___ Divide 45.86 by 10.

6. ___$i = prt$___ Write the formula used to find simple interest.

7. ___9___ Write the square root of 81.

8. ___81___ Square 9.

9. ___18___ Find the mean of 16; 23; 15; and 18.

10. ___9.3 mi.___ Convert 15 km to miles. Remember 1 km = .62 mi.

11. ___20% increase___ Find the percent of increase from $50 to $60.

12. ___15___ Find the games won if the team won 3 out of every 5 games, and they played 25 games.

Follow the directions. *5 each*

13. ___5x + 4___   Simplify $3x + 2(x + 2)$.

14. ___27 cu. in.___   Find the volume of a cube with an edge of 3 in.

15. ___$c^2 = a^2 + b^2$___   Write the Pythagorean formula.

16. ___4___   Divide -20 by -5.

17. ___180°___   Write the number of degrees in a triangle.

18. ___$x - 5$___   Express 5 less than x algebraically.

19. ___binomial___   Classify $5x + 2y$ as a monomial, binomial, or trinomial.

20. ___144 sq. in.___   Write the number of square inches in a square foot.

Name _____ Date _____ Score _____

TEST 12   *Basic Mathematics*
_____
Units 1–15

Write *true* or *false* in each blank. *1 each (10)*

1. ___true___ The hypotenuse is the longest side in a right triangle.

2. ___true___ The absolute value of –8 is 8.

3. ___false___ An isosceles triangle has three congruent sides.

4. ___false___ The cosine is the ratio between the length of the opposite leg to the length of the hypotenuse.

5. ___false___ The boiling point of water is 212 °C.

6. ___false___ The expression 28*xyz* has 4 terms.

7. ___false___ Shapes that have the same size and shape are said to be similar.

8. ___true___ The points where the sides of a polygon meet are called the vertexes.

9. ___true___ A heptagon is a seven-sided polygon.

10. ___false___ An acute angle has more than 90° but less than 180°.

Follow the directions. Show all of your work. *1 each (6)*

11. ___$A = \frac{1}{2}bh$___ Write the formula for finding the area of a triangle.

12. ___$i = prt$___ Write the simple interest formula.

13. ___$C = \pi d$___ Write the formula for finding the circumference of a circle using the diameter.

14. ___$V = \pi r^2 h$___ Write the formula for finding the volume of a cylinder.

15. ___$P = 4s$___ Write the formula for finding the perimeter of a square.

16. ___193 km___ Convert 120 miles to the nearest whole kilometer. Remember that 1 mi. = 1.61 km.

Follow the directions. Show all of your work. *1 each (13)*

17. _____113 °F._____ Convert 45 °C to the Fahrenheit scale.

18. _____1,587 mi._____ Find the approximate number of miles 23° North latitude is from the equator. Remember that the distance between 1° of latitude is approximately 69 miles.

19. _____1:35 A.M._____ Write the time in the Central Zone if the time in the Pacific Zone is 11:35 P.M.

20. _____350 cm_____ Write the number of centimeters in 3.5 meters.

21. _____$\frac{1}{4}$ in._____ Write the number of inches needed to represent 25 miles on a map if $\frac{1}{2}$ inch represents 50 miles.

22. _____56 oz._____ Write the number of ounces in $3\frac{1}{2}$ pounds.

23. _____0.58_____ Round off 0.579 to the nearest hundredth.

24. _____90°_____ Write the number of degrees in a right angle.

25. _____$x = 10$_____ Write the value of x in $\frac{5}{8} = \frac{x}{16}$.

26. _____3 cm_____ Write the length of the radius if the diameter is 6 cm.

27. _____–14_____ Write the sum of –6 and –8.

28. _____$6\frac{4}{5}$_____ Change $\frac{34}{5}$ to a mixed number.

29. _____.0025_____ Express $\frac{1}{4}$% as a decimal.

Find the answers. Show all of your work. *2 each (32)*

30. _____3,146_____

30. 4,732
     − 1,586

31. 486
     × 509

32. 1.43
     8.097
     + 6.54

31. _____247,374_____

32. _____16.067_____

33. _____.003528_____

33. .504
     × .007

34. $16\frac{2}{3}$
     − $7\frac{4}{5}$

35. $15\frac{7}{8}$
     $9\frac{1}{2}$
     + $6\frac{1}{3}$

34. _____$8\frac{13}{15}$_____

35. _____$31\frac{17}{24}$_____

36. _____5_____

36. $9\frac{3}{8} \times \frac{8}{15}$

37. $1\frac{1}{4} \div 2$

38. 25% of 600

37. _____$\frac{5}{8}$_____

38. _____150_____

39. 4 is what % of 80?

40. 75 is 30% of what number?

39. _____5%_____

40. _____250_____

41. 12 hr. 30 min.
     − 7 hr. 45 min.

42. 5 lb. 6 oz.
     ×   7

41. _____4 hr. 45 min._____

42. _____37 lb. 10 oz._____

43. _____3.54_____

43. 7.8 ⟌ 2 7.6 1 2

44. 9 ⟌ 5 (nearest hundredth)

44. _____.56_____

45. _____61_____

45. $6 + 7 \times 3^2 - 8 =$

Find the area. Show all of your work. *2 each (6)*

46. ___81 cm²___ square—$s = 9$ cm

47. ___27 sq. ft.___ triangle—$b = 9$ ft.; $h = 6$ ft.

48. ___135 m²___ trapezoid—$b_1 = 15$ m; $b_2 = 12$ m; $h = 10$ m

Find the volume. Show all of your work. *2 each (6)*

49. ___64 cu. in.___ cube—$e = 4$ in.

50. ___180 cu. ft.___ rectangular solid—$l = 10$ ft.; $w = 6$ ft.; $h = 3$ ft.

51. ___37.68 cm³___ cylinder—$r = 2$ cm; $h = 3$ cm

Solve and check the equations. Show all of your work. *1 each (4)*

52. ___$x = 5$___ $3x - 3 = 12$

53. ___$x = 15$___ $\frac{2}{3}x = 10$

54. ___$x = 5$___ $5x - 2x = 15$

55. ___$x = 4$___ $6x + 3 = 4x + 11$

Simplify. Show all of your work. *1 each (7)*

56. _____13_____ $8 - (-5) =$

57. _____-5_____ $\frac{-25}{5} =$

58. ___$11x + 5y$___ $5(x + y) + 6x =$

59. _____27_____ $3^3 =$

60. _____15_____ $\sqrt{225}$

61. _____24_____ $-8(-3) =$

62. _____-8_____ $(-2)^3 =$

Solve the word problems. Show all of your work. *1 each (6)*

63. _____$275_____   Jimmy Hale earns a $5\frac{1}{2}\%$ commission. Find his commission on sales of $5,000.

64. _____95_____   Amy's grades for her last five math tests were 95; 90; 100; 96; and 94. What is her mean grade?

65. _____$765_____   The list price of a refrigerator is $900. It is on sale for 15% off the list price. What is the sale price?

66. ___$92.25___   The Washington family used 1,230 kw-hr of electricity one month. Their rate is 7.5¢ per kw-hr. Find the amount of their electric bill.

67. _$.178 or 17.8¢_   An 18-ounce jar of peanut butter costs $3.20. Find the unit price to the nearest tenth of one cent.

68. ___$1,680___   Lane Davis borrowed $7,000 for 2 years at the rate of 12%. Find the amount of his simple interest.

Write an equation and solve. Show all of your work. *1 each part (8)*

69. <u>$n + 2n = 24$</u>   The sum of a number and twice the number is 24. What is the number?
        $n = 8$

70. <u>$x + 2x = 150$</u>   One angle has twice as many degrees as another angle. The sum of the
        $x = 50°$ degrees in both angles is 150°. How many degrees are in each angle?
        $2x = 100°$

71. <u>$x + 3x = 48$</u>   The sum of Mark's and his mom's ages is 48. His mom's age is three
      Mark—12 yr.   times his age. What is the age of each?
      Mom—36 yr.